The Open University

School of
HEALTH
&
SOCIAL
WELFARE

K100
Understanding Health and
Social Care

Block 4

Working with Life
Experience

K100 Production Team

Andrew Northedge (Chair)
Jan Walmsley (Deputy Chair)
Margaret Allott (Course Manager)
Tanya Hames (Course Secretary)
Joanna Bornat
Hilary Brown
Celia Davies
Roger Gomm
Sheila Peace
Martin Robb
Deborah Cooper (VQ Centre)

Jill Alger, Julie Fletcher (Editors); Janis Gilbert (Graphic Artist); Hannah Brunt, Rob Williams (Designers); Paul Smith (Librarian); Deborah Bywater (Project Control Assistant); Ann Carter (Print Buying Controller); Pam Berry (Text Processing Services); Mike Levers (Photographer); Vic Lockwood, Alison Tucker, Kathy Wilson (BBC Producers); Maggie Guillon (Cartoonist)

Regional Education and Training Managers

Lindsay Brigham
Anne Fletcher
Carole Ulanowsky

External Assessor

Professor Lesley Doyal, University of Bristol

This is the K100 core course team. Many other people also contributed to making the course and their names are given in the Introduction and Study Guide.

The Open University, Walton Hall, Milton Keynes, MK7 6AA

First published 1998

Designed, edited and typeset by The Open University

Printed and bound in the United Kingdom by Thanet Press

ISBN 0 7492 3423 7

For further information on related Open University courses and study packs, write to The Information Officer, School of Health and Social Welfare, The Open University, Walton Hall, Milton Keynes MK7 6AA.

1.1

17373B/k100b4u14i1.1

Contents

Study skills by Andrew Northedge

Introduction

We have seen how caring relationships are located within particular places and also within families, communities and wider society. But care relationships are also located within people's personal life stories. How you experience a care relationship depends not only on where and how that happens but also on what it means within your own life. In this block we look at the ways in which life experience can become much more at the centre of caring and supporting relationships. Sometimes this means giving people the time to explore who they are, where they've come from and how they feel about themselves today, and in the past. It may mean encouraging carers to listen to life experiences and life stories, so that with a much fuller picture of who someone is they may be able to offer sympathetic and appropriate support. It may mean developing an awareness of how accounts of the past can be shaped by experiences of the present, or be used by groups of people to determine the nature of the care and support they are seeking. It may be recognising that what someone has to say about their experience of care is a contribution to an understanding of attitudes towards users of care services and care workers in the past. It may be a way of measuring how much caring work and the experience of care has changed, or stayed the same over time.

Unit 14
Lives

Prepared for the course team by Joanna Bornat with additional material from Andrew Northedge

While you are working on Unit 14, you will need:
- Course Reader
- Offprints Book
- Audio Cassette 4
- Media Notes
- Wallchart

Contents

Introduction

There is a knot inside me
A knot which cannot be untied
Strong
It hurts
As if they had put a stone
Inside of me
I always remember the old days
Playing at our summer house
Going to grandmother's
Staying at grandmother's
I want those days to return
Perhaps the knot will be untied when they return
But there is a knot inside of me
So strong
It hurts
As if it is a stone inside of me.

(Eight-year-old Turkish girl, quoted in Ryan and Walker, 1993)

I often wonder why people bother with people like us. I could have reeled it off for what you are doing: it's a life story; it's the biography of the person you are writing about; it's me. If you have the time and the inclination that is.

(Jane Arnell, aged 85, in the Reader, Chapter 15)

In this block we focus on individual lives. So far in the course we've been introduced to many different people and learnt from them something of the way they live and how they experience care and support and take action for themselves. So what else could we need to know about individual lives? Perhaps the two quotations above give a clue.

The eight-year-old Turkish girl and Jane Arnell both mention 'me' and they are saying something about stories from their pasts. The child tells us briefly about a part of her life that she remembers. Jane Arnell mentions 'a life story'. They both want to say something about themselves, to release hurtful emotions in the case of the young girl, to tell the story of 'the person' as Jane Arnell explains. She's perhaps emphasising that, despite the effects of her dementing illness, her memory loss and difficulties in communication, she's still there. As she says, 'it's me'.

Why should knowing about 'me' and 'a life story' be important? Most of the time people tend to be fairly confident about who they are, who they feel they used to be and what they want to be, but there are some situations when the links between who they feel they were and who they are now become obscured or lost. The Turkish girl is remembering some good things from her past to help her deal with other painful things in her life. Her poem is sometimes used, carefully, by social workers with groups of children who are making life story books as they prepare for adoption and fostering (Ryan and Walker, 1993, p. 53). Children who have not lived with their birth parents need help to recover their pasts and to find ways to deal with separation and loss if they are to 'move on' and develop emotionally and socially with confidence. In this way, remembering becomes a central activity in the expression of identity.

People who need or are receiving care may find that the identity props on which they, and most people, rely are fragile or threatened in some way. They may be going through major life changes: losing partners, friends and contemporaries as they grow older; losing mobility or sensual or intellectual capacity. They may have to move from somewhere they are closely attached to into a quite new, even frightening, environment. Sometimes lack of paid work or the shift into parenthood or becoming a carer means that roles and activities change or there are new places and relationships to get used to or become known in. When there are changes like these one approach is not to focus on the nature of the illness or the immediate problem someone is presenting but on the whole person. This may mean providing an opportunity for someone to talk about themselves and their past experience. By focusing on the whole person in this way, it may be possible to make care practice more sensitive and individualised, and improve the quality of life and care relationships.

In this unit I'll be asking the following core questions:

Core questions

- Why is a sense of identity so important?

- What factors threaten a sense of identity?

- How can identity be maintained and supported in adverse circumstances?

- How best can people be supported in communicating their identity?

Section 1
Life experience as everyday talk

We've been focusing on why talking about our own personal experience may be important in care relationships, but isn't talking about your own life something that goes on all the time?

Activity 1 **The personal as public property**

This is the sort of activity you can do as and when. Just carry on with the unit at present and keep an eye out for any personal stories in your leisure time.

When you've got a moment, or feel like taking a short break from this unit, check through the newspapers, magazines, television, radio and film listings, books and adverts which have come your way recently. How many of them carry a personal story about the past or include someone talking about their own life as an illustration or source of information? We've assembled a few examples in the collage overleaf. Looking through them, what kind of messages do you think they attempt to convey?

Comment You might find yourself overwhelmed by the amount of personal detail that's available. You might also have noticed that personal history and biography has found its way into all sorts of different kinds of information: advertising, fundraising, leisure activities, entertainment. The messages in the clippings included in the collage seem to be about identifying with the people shown by calling up emotions and experiences which may be shared. Personalising accounts with stories of real people, or making them seem real by quoting their words, using their actual names, or showing images from earlier in their lives makes it more likely that we'll pause and get 'hooked' by what we read. Sometimes these images are difficult to pass by.

Life stories are everywhere. In adverts, magazines, music, sport, politics, chat shows, the messages we get are personalised through interviews and stories which tell us about quite intimate details of people's lives, feelings, emotions and even what feel like secrets. Autobiography and personal accounts have also become increasingly common means of revealing different versions of the past, with television and radio programmes focusing on 'ordinary' life events or the stories of 'ordinary' people. The better-known entertain with personal histories in 'Desert Island Discs', 'In the Psychiatrist's Chair' and 'This is Your Life'. Family historians draw on the stories people tell about their relatives to research their family trees. Publishers record greater-than-ever sales for biographies and autobiographies. And it seems that the demand for opportunities to talk about oneself has never been higher. Counselling activities now account for a large part of the job market. It has been estimated that 'over 2.5 million use counselling as a major part of their job' (Persaud, 1993, pp. 8–9).

Biography and autobiography go back a long way. But it seems that it was in the nineteenth century that interest really took off. For example, life stories as examples of achievement were very popular. The most famous of these was Samuel Smiles' classic study *Self Help*, first published in 1859, which included examples of famous businessmen, artists and scientists. Other nineteenth century writers celebrated their

WE'RE NOT FREAKS ...

Being a dwarf was tough in Gladys' day. Happily, three generations on, things have changed ...

When Gladys Brooks was born a dwarf-height parents in 1932, shocked relatives said it was because her mum believed in fairies.

'Nobody knew anything about dwarfism then, so I spent my childhood in and out of hospital,' recalls Gladys, from Over, Cambridgeshire. 'I was strapped to a frame for three and a half years in an attempt to straighten my spine. I was experimented on, stretched on climbing frames until my sockets were loosened, and paraded at lectures by my GP. I felt like a freak!.

WE'RE PROUD TO BE SMALL!

(*Woman*, 2 June 1997, p.52)

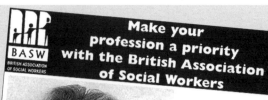

Maria Rantho says she's pushy

grew up in a black township in South Africa

trained as a nurse

was paralysed in a car accident

joined a self-help group, supported by CAFOD

campaigns for disabled rights

laughs loudly

has now become her country's first disabled MP

Throughout the Third World ordinary people are doing extraordinary things with support from CAFOD

MY JOB

I always end up taking work home with me

I'm a single mum and it's very tough being the sole breadwinner. I feel that I've got to do well in my job to provide security for my daughter, Olivia – she drives me to push myself hard at work.

(Natasha Price, from *Woman*, 2 June 1997, p.31)

Who would have thought...

...we would be spending our anniversary going back to the same hotel, after all these years.

For just £16 a year everyone in Britain, aged 60 and over, can enjoy one-third off rail travel.

(*Active Life*, July/August 1996)

MUM KNOWS BEST

This section of the magazine is dedicated to teaching our generation how to cook African and Caribbean dishes as well as mum.

(*Pride*, May 1997, p.112)

Personal experience seems to get into everything

religious conversion, while others again, as working men, wrote accounts of their lives for the entertainment of better-off sections of society (Thompson, 1988, pp. 34–35). In 1831, Mary Prince, a runaway ex-slave living in England, published her autobiography, *The History of Mary Prince* (Ferguson, 1993). It became a bestseller and a major contribution to the campaign to abolish the slavery of black people. Other nineteenth century reformers drew directly on the experiences of poor people to shock their audiences into action. The journalist Henry Mayhew interviewed child workers in London streets around 1850. One of his most poignant accounts came from an eight-year-old girl working as a watercress seller who told him:

> *On and off, I've been very near a twelvemonth in the streets. Before that, I had to take care of a baby for my aunt. No, it wasn't heavy – it was only twelve months old; but I minded it for ever such a time – till it could walk. It was a very nice little baby, not a very pretty one; but if I touched it under the chin, it would laugh. Before I had the baby, I used to help mother, who was in the fur trade; and if there was any slits in the fur, I'd sew them up. My mother learned me to needlework and to knit when I was about five...*
>
> *(Quoted in Davin, 1996, p. 158)*

Original illustration from Henry Mayhew's London Labour and the London Poor, *1861–2*

More recently, disabled people have used their own personal histories to develop a collective awareness of themselves as a group sharing the same struggles against a disabling society. Barbara Lisicki remembers:

> *I wasn't a stranger to impairments because it had been born into my family, both my father and brother had impairments. Actually, my consciousness was from a very early age of really having to fight other people's voyeurism and curiosity. Me and my other brother used to pile in the noddy car with Andrew and we used to drive around. But when people used to stare at us when we went out together I used to say 'What do you think you are staring at?' Even as a kid I was on one level challenging people's behaviour towards disabled people even though I wasn't a disabled person at that time.*

> (Quoted in Campbell and Oliver, 1996, p. 36)

Telling about your past experience, autobiography, is not just a question of ensuring that the record of the past is complete and representative. What also seems to be important is a *need* to tell. Giddens discusses the way in which self-identity is sustained through the constant retelling of biographical stories, drawing in new experiences, relating to other people and says that these are resources, helpful because: 'a sense of self-identity is often securely enough held to weather major tensions or transitions in the social environments within which the person moves' (Giddens, 1991, p. 55).

The playwright Dennis Potter was someone for whom a personal sense of the past was clearly important. Though he used popular songs to evoke memories in his TV plays 'Pennies from Heaven' and 'The Singing Detective', he resisted the idea that this might be simply nostalgia:

> *... your own culture, your own language, your own communality which you shared with your forebears – is actually shaping the future, too. It's people without a sense of the past who are alienated and rootless, and they're losers; they lose out.*

> *To make any political statement you first of all have to know who and what you are; what shaped your life, what is possible and what isn't. That's not nostalgia. That's a kind of grappling with the past – an ache for it, perhaps sometimes a contempt for it. But the past commingles with everything you do and everything you project forward.*

> (Quoted in Fuller, 1993, p. 23)

Dennis Potter is suggesting that people fashion identities from those bits of their past which enable them to cope with changes in society and the uncertainties and complexities they have to cope with on a daily basis. He makes a link between the past and the present. We use our memories of what was to tell ourselves the story of who we are now. Psychologists see this telling and narrating as beginning very early in life, often before children acquire proper speech. In this way our memories about ourselves come about through interactions with others, usually our parents. Here's an example where Paul (4 years 3 months) and Rebecca (5 years 10 months) are looking at photographs with their mother:

> Mother: *Do you remember being on this beach?*

> Paul: *yuk, no.*

> Mother: *don't you, when we went to Jersey, on the aeroplane, do you not remember that?*

Sharing memories

Paul: *is that Jersey?*

Mother: *mm, look Rebecca's wearing a hat that says Jersey on it.*

Paul: *look, what is that?*

Mother: *[...] probably a book – we were going to go on that boat or a trip down the river and we took one or two books to keep you two occupied.*

(Middleton and Edwards, 1990, p. 40)

Paul's mother not only prompted him and helped him to recall events, she also showed him *how* to remember, by pointing out clues like his sister's hat and the book. It is in such ways that remembering becomes very much part of our inner lives, helping us to build up meaningful accounts of who we are.

The importance of protecting memory is something which is emphasised in what are called Preparation Groups, where carers learn about the many different aspects of fostering and adoption. One activity invites them to 'randomly list' their own memories of childhood, both good and bad. The group facilitator writes these onto a flip chart and when there are plenty of 'memories' the list is torn in two. This dramatic action is meant as a reminder that this is what can happen to children's memories if they are not 'held' and protected by their carers. The group then goes on to discuss how carers can help children to hold and develop their memories.

Establishing an identity by remembering events from the past can be an important way of building links and establishing what is shared and common in groups of people as well as among people whose life experience may have been quite isolating or distant from what are seen as 'normal' life events. Atkinson found in her work with a group of older men and women with learning difficulties that by telling their experiences of hospital life they were able to identify shared memories and 'spark off' forgotten ones. The group was going through the experience of leaving hospital and moving into the community. It was particularly important for them to be able to individualise their past experience because they were people who had been living institutionalised lives; it was also important for them to build up an account of hospital life which they could cope with and not continue to feel oppressed by. She includes an example from Godfrey and Marjorie who happened to be in the same hospital at the same time:

Marjorie: *After 20 years we changed over, and it was Sister 'Smith'.*

Godfrey: *Was she on the children's ward?*

Marjorie: *She was on F2. And then we had 'Moffat'. She was on F1. She died in the end.*

Godfrey: *She was a wicked old devil, she was! No wonder she died!*

Marjorie: *Old devil?*

Godfrey: *Yes!*

Marjorie: *You're telling me! And Smith!*

(Atkinson, 1993, p. 101)

Not only were Godfrey and Marjorie and the other members of this group able to talk about their own individual experiences but through sharing their memories they also began to develop a particular group experience of hospital life. Sharing memories of long-term hospitalisation was painful for this group but they found that they could share some humorous memories of those times as well.

Activity 2   Different memories and shared memories

Allow about 10 minutes   Look back through some of the quotes and images included so far in this unit. Do any of the accounts remind you of things that have happened in your own life? They may have been pleasant or painful memories. Perhaps things came back that you thought you had forgotten. Perhaps certain words triggered off particular memories to do with holidays, first experiences of training in a hospital, or perhaps it was an association with a television programme or particular piece of advertising. Jot down some key words for yourself as a reminder and add any particular things you associate with them. These might be places, people or things about yourself.

Comment   Holidays: I looked back and remembered a holiday in North Berwick when I was eight – my mother and I stayed at a hotel where we got to know lots of strangers. Car journeys: being sick in the back of my uncle's new car – I think it was the combination of the smell of the leatherette seats and the matches he kept striking to light his pipe.

One of our course testers found this activity '... almost amusing! I was amazed at what I remembered. Falling in a bed of nettles, school dinners complete with a caterpillar, living with my grandma ... and much more.'

We've seen that talking about the past and listening to accounts of personal experience has become a popular and well documented activity. But why are stories and memories from people's pasts important for work in health and social care? Drawing on what you've just read there are a number of key points to be made.

Key points

- Giving attention to memories means sharing and recognising aspects of each other's lives and perhaps acknowledging and understanding differences in experience.

- Memories help to make public accounts which enlighten and serve to raise awareness of hidden or stigmatised experience. Henry Mayhew was something of a pioneer in that respect.

- Encouraging people to talk about the past can be a way of helping them to manage change in their lives and establish identity in the present.

In the rest of this unit we go on to look at some of these issues in more detail and to consider some explanations about the development and expression of identity at different life stages. Drawing on examples from childhood, the middle years of life and old age we look at examples of how talk about the past can help in the development of supportive strategies and lead to sensitive and appropriate practice with individual people. We begin with an example of life story work with a young person who has experienced fostering and residential childcare.

Section 2
Working with memories – life story books

Life story books are used more and more by social workers, residential care staff and some foster parents with young people who, for various reasons, need to find ways to remember and talk about earlier parts of their lives. The books may take a variety of forms: photograph albums, scrapbooks, written accounts and audio and video recordings. They may include drawings, poems, family trees, letters, bus and train tickets, photographs, writing and all sorts of ephemera that evoke the past, or provide clues to identity and individual histories. Children who grow up in the families they are born into usually have plenty of opportunities to find out about their parents and wider family members, the places they have lived in and the reasons for any changes they've experienced. Children who experience separation from their birth families often face greater obstacles when it comes to finding out about parents, grandparents, homes and communities they've lived in. There may be gaps and difficult areas in accounts of their identity and they may have to work out ways of dealing with difficult memories and emotions. They need to be able to explain what has happened to them and to move on to develop plans for the future. People working with children find that a life story book can help a child to talk about losses, changes and separations and to remember the good things they've experienced too.

Jamie Knight is 21. He lives with his girlfriend and baby daughter. He hasn't lived with both his parents since he was five. He's experienced many changes in his life. We recorded him talking to Sarah Burrows, who used to be his residential care keyworker, about how they made a life story book when he was 10.

Activity 3   **Life story work**

Allow about 30 minutes

On the beach at Southend: Jamie aged 10 with Sarah Burrows

Jamie Knight at the time of the K100 recording

Listen to the first side of Audio Cassette 4. You may need to listen to Jamie and Sarah twice while you make notes.

While you are listening, note down:

(a)   some of the things Jamie mentions collecting for his life story book
(b)   some of the feelings and emotions he and Sarah mention while they were making the book.

Comment   (a)   Some of the things Jamie mentions are: the date his mum and dad were married and his birth date, 'all written on nice little cards', some of his own writing, some baby photos, pictures of him taken outside his father's and mother's houses, more dates and several photos taken by his first foster mother, photos of himself and his foster mother when he went back to Southend, a picture taken of the social services building, photos from the time he was in residential care, his birth certificate and photos taken when he was advertised for fostering as a teenager.

(b)   Jamie and Sarah mention various feelings and emotions. Jamie says making the book was 'good'. Sarah says he was 'an angry little boy, very upset, abandoned ...'. She says it was 'hard' and 'quite overwhelming' going back to see his foster mother while they were researching what to put in the book, because it was 'somebody from your past'. The picture of the social services building is 'sad' to Jamie. Sarah points out that the 'pictures and things' don't really show the whole process which was actually 'difficult for Jamie to do', particularly remembering his mother whom he hadn't seen since he was five (and still hasn't).

One of our course testers who was abused as a child said that she could 'totally relate' to the process that Jamie went through. She had felt almost anonymous, without a childhood, until she was 40. Once she realised that she had been emotionally abused she was able to understand why she had never loved her mother. She says she is certain that knowing about her childhood is important to her as an adult. When she became able to remember what happened her feelings about her mother became acceptable to her.

 It's important to note that some of the things that happened to Jamie couldn't happen today. The 1989 Children Act (England and Wales) no longer allows what Sarah describes as 'the voluntary care route' through which his father put him into care when he was eight, although it does allow for children to be 'accommodated' at the request of those with parental responsibility. And of course we'd hope that in working with a child like Jamie social workers might be more careful to help him keep more of the photographs and personal things which anyone needs to look back through their lives. Making life story books with children who have become separated from their original families is now established as good practice, particularly since the Children Act of 1989 with its emphasis on partnership in working relationships with parents and carers. Tony Ryan and Roger Walker have helped children make life story books for many years – they emphasise that good practice means 'listening to children and respecting their views' but also warn that it may not always be appropriate for every child and that it should never be used as a substitute for 'skilled and long-term therapy' (Ryan and Walker, 1993, p. 4). Nevertheless they argue that:

Life story work can increase a child's sense of self-esteem, because, sadly, at the back of the minds of nearly all children separated from their families of origin is the thought that they are worthless and unlovable. They blame themselves for the actions of adults.

(p. 6)

Ryan and Walker stress the importance of identity and point out that the 'creation of the idea of "self" is crucial to healthy development' and that children who have been 'severed from their roots and [who are] without a clear future' can be helped if they 'talk about the past, the present and the future' (pp. 6–7). Sarah Burrows started the life history with Jamie Knight at a time when he was about to be fostered. She saw it as a way to help him talk about his feelings and perhaps not blame himself or his parents for his past as part of preparation for the future. Jamie had very little left of his early years. Just a few things seem to stand out. At one point when Sarah asks him about his visits to his dad's new family he says 'I can't really remember, I can only remember things that are written down here.' The importance to Jamie of piecing together these fragments comes through very strongly, particularly since his own file was destroyed in a fire.

For Jamie, as with other young people who become involved in making life story books, this is a process which has no end. He points out that he can go on adding to it now and it has helped him to remember things about his sister from whom he became separated when he was taken into care and whom he's now thinking of contacting.

Activity 4   **Life story work: developing awareness**

Allow about 20 minutes

Turn to Offprint 18. This is the introduction to Ryan and Walker's book, *Life Story Work*, I quoted from above. Read through the offprint and, as you do, note down:

(a) some of the basic principles they advocate as essential for this work

(b) how many of these principles you would say apply only to work with children and young people.

Comment   (a)   The basic principles I noted down included:

Rights: 'children are entitled to an accurate knowledge of their past and families'.

Patience and sensitivity: the process may take time and may develop at a varied pace over days; letting the child be the guide to what is to be told and how.

Confidentiality: being trustworthy and being aware that a child might be telling a private story that is not for public consumption.

(b)   You may have felt like me that on just about every point these principles might apply at any age or stage of life or situation. However, where an adult is concerned there might be a question raised over how family members might be involved or participate. This might be particularly important in relation to people with learning disabilities whose status as adults may not easily be accepted by parents. Think back to Lynne and her father and ask yourself how easy it would be for her to make her own life story book with her father's involvement and participation.

Key points

- Children who have had experience of separation and loss in their lives can be helped to deal with this through finding ways to tell their life stories.

- Life story work is as much about dealing with the present and preparing for the future as it is sorting out feelings about the past.

- Life story work may not be appropriate for every child and the child's wishes should be respected at all stages.

- There are basic principles in life story work which could apply at any age or stage of life.

Study skills: Managing your essay writing

Early in Block 3 we suggested that you looked ahead to TMA 03. How did that work out? Did it help you to stay focused as you were reading the units? Did it help with writing the essay? Have you had any new ideas since for setting about the writing of your next essay? What are your plans for TMA 04? Have you already looked at it, or should you look now?

Section 3
Identity and life stages

The word 'identity' has cropped up frequently in the course so far. In talking about life story work with children and young people, Ryan and Walker emphasise that 'A healthy sense of identity is vital to everybody' (1993, p. 6). What does 'identity' mean? Looking the word up in a dictionary is one way to find out. I tried the Chambers English Dictionary and found the following definition:

> ... state of being the same: sameness; individuality; personality: who or what a person or thing is ...

This works well for everyday speech and discussion, but from a sociologist's or a psychologist's point of view it misses out some important aspects of how identity exists in everyday life, how people use it, maintain it or develop it. I suggest that identity is whatever someone *thinks* or *feels* they are. The sociologist Anthony Giddens refines the concept of identity further with the idea of 'self identity'. He is interested in how people actively develop and adopt ideas and meanings about themselves and how they sustain them in relation to the challenges, complexities and anxieties of living (Giddens, 1991).

We're now going to look at identity in greater depth and discuss why knowing about identity is important and useful and how it develops from the earliest years of life.

3.1 Do you need an identity?

We have been talking about life story work and talking about the past as a way of confirming identities. But why is identity important? What do you need an identity for?

Activity 5   **Identity in our lives**

Allow about 15 minutes

Do you feel you have an identity? Can you remember times when you have felt uncertain of your identity? If so, what caused the uncertainty? What was the effect on you of this uncertainty? Jot down a few thoughts.

To help you think about this, draw a line to represent your life as our course tester did in the comment below. Mark on it the things which you feel have been important to you. These might be turning points or changes. Add on the ages when these occurred.

When you've finished look at it to see if there are any obvious stages which relate to particular ages. How would you describe these? Are any of them particularly important or significant? Looking at the line, do you feel you always had the same identity?

Comment   Perhaps the most straightforward way of answering the first question is simply to give your name and address. Someone who commented on this unit remembered how, when he was a child, he wrote after his name and address, 'Great Britain, The World, The Universe'. Perhaps it was his way of expressing his sense of identity as someone very small inside something extremely large. Strictly, your identity is what marks you off from other people as a particular individual, so one way of distinguishing

Born Monday March 5th 1945

—— Friday 13th April 1945 – Father drowned (see Note 1)

—— September 1949 – started school (Note 2)

—— 1951 – Brother went to do National Service (Note 3)

—— 1952 – at the Cenotaph on Remembrance Day. I realised why I had no Dad. (Note 4)

—— 1952 – Grandma died

—— Sep 1956 – started High School

—— Sep 1961 – started work

—— Oct 1965 – got married

—— Nov 1966 – 1st son born – mother married (Note 5)

—— April 1968 – 2nd son born

—— March 1970 – daughter born

—— Oct 1970 – divorced

—— Nov 1973 – married the father of my daughter

—— July 1980 – divorced again – husband alcoholic

—— 1987 – got married again. Got it right this time!!

—— April 1990 – was with my stepfather when he died

—— 1991 – 82-year-old mother developed osteoporosis (Note 6)

—— 1993 – I am diagnosed as having ME

—— July 1993 – grandson born

—— May 1994 – granddaughter born

—— May 1996 – another granddaughter born

Notes

Note 1 – I obviously could not remember this date at the time, but it became very important to me in later life.

Note 2 – When I started school, I always wondered why I didn't have a Dad like the other children, but I never asked, and was never told.

Note 3 – My brother is 15 years older than me, and I suppose he took the place of my Dad, when he went into the Army I felt that I had lost him.

Note 4 – The most traumatic day of my life. I remember vividly the scream I let out as it dawned on me why I had no Dad. I was only seven at the time but I can recall it as yesterday.

Note 5 – Although my stepfather was a wonderful husband to my mother, and she certainly deserved some happiness, I always felt that he had come between us.

Note 6 – I have to do virtually everything for my mother. It is very hard coping with her and my ME. I feel that now all my children are settled life should be easier, but it is just the opposite.

A course tester's lifeline

yourself might be to quote your National Insurance number, or your passport number. If that were what was meant, then I would definitely be uncertain of my identity, since I can never remember these numbers, or where to find them.

But I bet when you thought about feelings of uncertainty about your identity you did not have anything like that in mind. It isn't at the level of names and numbers that anxieties arise. When I thought about identity doubts, I thought about times of major change in my life, like leaving school or feeling disconnected from things – living alone in a big city or doing work I felt unsuited to among people I found hard to relate to. Uncertainties about identity are more to do with pondering over such questions as 'Where do I fit into the world? What is the point of my life? Who am I important to?' In other words, questions about the meaning of your life, both to yourself and to other people. This is what we mean by identity in this unit – your sense of your particular place within the flow of life going on around you. You'll remember in Unit 7 we saw how where someone lives can be at the heart of identity and feelings about self and membership of particular groups and communities.

In drawing your line did you become aware of the different person you seemed to be through all the stages – the child, the teenager, the adult? Did you feel as if the mind you thought with then didn't view things or think about them as you do now? Or did you feel a thread of continuity? Perhaps you felt no sudden transition at which you became the person you are now but as you drew your line you might have been aware of differences. If you can, compare your life line with one drawn for someone else (or the one shown here drawn by someone who tested this unit at an early stage). Not everyone goes through the same stages at the same time, or ever. Not everyone becomes a parent and some people only become parents well after others become grandparents. People with learning difficulties, like Lynne in Unit 1, find that their way into adult status is blocked. She's in her 40s now and still hasn't been able to leave home.

For our purposes identities are to do with *meanings,* in particular the meanings we give to ourselves and to our lives. You'll remember how in Unit 4 we explored Goffman's ideas about the way groups of people develop meanings together – 'defining scenes' and 'presenting themselves' within them. We also talked about social reality being 'socially constructed' – in other words, the 'world' we are aware of living in being one we, as a society, construct for ourselves.

Since people 'understand' the world through making it meaningful to themselves – since everything is invested with meaning – people must also make *themselves* meaningful. Otherwise there is a terrible gap in the world, in the very place each person occupies. The picture as a whole cannot make proper sense unless you can make some sense of yourself. This isn't something you do once for all time. You keep doing it on a daily basis. Meanings shift. New questions arise. Sometimes life is busy and underlying questions about its meaning get submerged. But always, in the background, there is, for most people, an urge to secure for yourself a sense of who you are and what your significance is within your family, neighbourhood, community or wider society.

So how does this sense of identity, or personal meaningfulness, develop? To explore this we are going to look at the work of Erik Erikson.

Erik Erikson (1902–94)

Erikson was born in Germany of Danish parents. He trained and practised as a psychoanalyst in Austria but emigrated to America to escape Nazi persecution in the 1930s. During the war he worked in a rehabilitation clinic for war veterans. Subsequently he worked with adolescent patients. He was particularly interested in comparing the processes of growing up in different cultures and made a study of two tribes of Native Americans.

He was also a proponent of 'psycho-biography', using narrative methods to analyse the lives of famous people.

He published his most famous book, *Childhood and Society*, in 1950 (at the same time as Bowlby was writing the work we studied in Unit 1).

3.2 Erikson's eight stages of identity development

Erikson sees growing up as a process of forming our inner being – our thoughts, emotions, and life goals – in a way which is adapted to the society each person lives in. He focuses on how people 'make sense of themselves' as they go about the tasks of daily life. People shape themselves to fit society and in the process make themselves meaningful within society. But this quest for personal meaning takes different forms at different times of our lives. He sees individuals as facing a series of challenges, each of which comes to the fore at a particular stage of life. There's an interesting aspect to Erikson's model of eight stages which makes it particularly relevant to K100: unlike Freud's, it covers the *whole* of life, from infancy to old age.

Activity 6   **From infancy to adulthood**

Allow about 10 minutes

Now turn to Offprint 19 by Erikson: 'Eight ages of man'. Read through the first five stages of Erikson's model and make some brief notes on what you think each stage means. If you can think of any experiences which match what he suggests make a note of them too.

By the way, following the convention of the time, Erikson's babies and children are, like Bowlby's, all male, and they are looked after by mothers. You might like to look out for any other similarities with Bowlby's account of this first year of life.

Comment   1   **Basic trust v. basic mistrust**. When Erikson talks of 'an inner population of remembered and anticipated sensations and images' he means the beginnings of what Bowlby calls an internal 'working

Smile for Grandpa...

model' of the world. He is saying that there are all these things going on inside the baby and they correspond with the things going on outside the baby. And just as the things outside become familiar, so the things inside become familiar, and the baby gradually becomes confident that the two sets go together. In other words, the baby's internal body sensations and mental processes 'reflect' the world outside.

The 'consistency, continuity, and sameness of experience' – feeding routines, nappy changing, and so on – provides a **patterning** out of which meanings can be built. Being repeatedly absorbed, as a participant, within these purposeful, caring activities, embeds the baby's experience within the meanings of the immediate environment. Erikson says this is the basis from which we develop a sense that life is meaningful and are able to approach the later challenges of life with a general sense of trust.

However, if the baby's experience is not consistent – if it often happens that internal discomfort and crying do **not** correspond with any outward action to alleviate them – the baby will be more inclined towards mistrust. He will not develop a basis for confidence that life is meaningful. Erikson is not saying that we develop **either** trust **or** mistrust by the time we are one year old. He says that we are pulled between the two, and continue to be all our lives.

2   **Autonomy v. shame and doubt**. Having established a kind of 'oneness' with her surroundings – an absorption into its ongoing meanings – the next step is to acquire a sense of having a separate existence – a will of her own. Instead of being always caught up with the flow of the meanings projected by carers, the small child begins to participate more actively, by resisting these meanings. The clearest demonstration of an independent will is to oppose the will of others. Resistance becomes a major exercise in identity development.

But in spite of the **appearance** of opposition, Erikson warns us that the child is also afraid of upsetting the established relationship of trust – the base from which he has the confidence to act. Establishing a separate will through opposition feels like a dangerous learning process – risking all that is good and meaningful. Parents must control firmly but reassuringly. The child must not develop a general sense that he has ruined everything and been cast into shame, or shaken the foundations of meaning.

3   **Initiative v. guilt**. Having exercised independence simply through opposition, the child moves on to develop a more genuine independence through developing projects of his own.

By this stage (from around five or six years to around 10), the child is imagining himself as an adult through games involving role-playing. One of the games is to play at being a parent – '**identifying**' with the parent of the same sex. Erikson says that simply by having his own aims and plans, the child encounters a sense of guilt that the plans would not be approved by his parent. In other words, the child develops a conscience – the capability of being self-critical. This is where the danger lies at this stage. Because parents and teachers are too strict, or else not strict enough, the capacity to feel guilty develops too strongly and the child's sense of initiative is stunted.

4   **Industry v. inadequacy.** From 10 years, according to Erikson, children begin to accept a need to move beyond 'pretend' adult activities. They become interested in developing skills and knowledge which will enable them to take on adult roles.

If children come to feel unsuccessful in engaging with these adult skills, then they have difficulty imagining themselves successfully fulfilling adult roles. At Stage 2 they risk developing a general **sense of shame** about themselves, as a result of their resistance to their parents; however at Stage 3 they risk developing a general **sense of guilt** about themselves, as a result of harbouring plans which society (their parents) might not approve of. At this fourth stage they risk developing a general **sense of inadequacy** about themselves as future members of adult society.

5   **Identity v. role confusion**. Up to this point in her life the child's sense of herself has largely been defined by adults: parents and teachers. Where she lives, what kind of a household she lives in, what standards she should behave to, what values she should respect, what roles she is encouraged to play and what she is barred from, have all been imposed by the preceding generation. But adulthood implies personal responsibility for these things. The child has to create a proper psychological 'identity' of her own by reaching out towards adulthood and relinquishing reliance on parents and teachers to frame her life's meaning. Just as the move from Stage 1 to Stage 2 involved a shift from **absorption** into the parents' will to **resistance** to it – so Stage 5 involves a shift from absorption into the childhood world defined by parents and teachers, to resistance to it. The very 'continuity and sameness' of the family setting, which earlier made meaning possible, must now be left behind. This requires experiments with alternative frames of reference **not** supplied by the preceding generation.

Erikson portrays adolescence as a time of turmoil. The whole basis of the young person's sense of self is reworked to form, for the first time, a true identity – former mentors temporarily become adversaries – and selected cliques of peers become the central focus of allegiance and identification. As a defence against identity confusion adolescents 'over-identify' with 'heroes' and are ready to become intensely committed to causes which supply a clearly defined identity. (Is being a 'football hooligan' an example of what Erikson calls 'rituals, creeds and programmes', with its chanting, its prejudices about rival supporters, and its series of journeys to away games?) The implication is that, as a secure adult identity develops, a lot of these allegiances and intense identifications drop away.

Erikson does not see identity as 'finalised' by the end of adolescence, but as continuing through three further stages in adult life.

Activity 7   **The three adult stages**

Allow about 10 minutes

Now read the last three short sections of Offprint 19 and make your own notes on what you think Erikson is saying.

Do these strike a chord with you? Can you see your own identity developing through stages like these? What about other people you know?

Jot down your reactions.

Comment   6   **Intimacy v. isolation**. Having established an independent adult identity within society – a sense of who you are, and of the meaningfulness of your life – you have the capability of making your own way within society. Provided that the struggles of the adolescent stage have enabled you to achieve a sufficiently independent identity, you will have the confidence to hitch your identity to another person's, without fear of losing it. As with the previous stages, there

is a struggle. The challenge is to do so in a way that allows you to experience intimacy while retaining a sense of your own self. Through 'competitive and combative relationships' you negotiate an outcome in which elements of the independence of each partner are (inevitably) compromised, but to which both come to have a sense of ethical commitment.

7   **Generativity v. stagnation**. The present only makes sense as both a development out of what has gone before and a projection towards an imagined future. No purposes have meaning unless society is seen as having a future. And, says Erikson, to be fully implicated in the future of society is to be committed to preparing a new generation to take over from one's own. Thus a fundamental source of life-meaning is to become engaged in producing and guiding the next generation. Not everyone is involved directly in parenthood. Some generate products or ideas which live on after them. However, in one way or another, says Erikson, we need to identify ourselves with those who follow us. Otherwise we stagnate, locked within the meanings of our own personal existence, with no future to direct ourselves towards beyond our own life span.

8   **Ego integrity v. despair**. Erikson sees the eighth stage as a time of pondering the overall meanings of life – of placing it in a wider context of lives in other times and places. In doing so, and in contemplating your own life in a spirit of acceptance, you come to terms with death. This is not only an achievement for yourself, but also helps to allay the anxieties of those working their way through the earlier stages. In a sense, each stage derives its meaning as a preparation for what lies ahead at the next stage. But the void of death at the end of the line threatens to undermine all the preceding meanings. So the achievement by the oldest generation of a strong sense of life's meaning and an accommodation with death, affirms the meaning of life all the way back down the line.

3.3 How helpful is Erikson's model?

Erikson's model has been very influential, particularly his account of his fifth stage – adolescence – which was his specialist field. His account of adolescence captures the imagination – those symbolic struggles with the challenge of adulthood. In fact, the transition from childhood to adulthood has been regarded as a special time in many societies. Often it has been marked with a ritual or ceremony known as a 'rite of passage', signalling to the community that the former child is now a proper member of society with all the rights and responsibilities of adulthood.

Yet research has tended to throw cold water on this dramatic picture. Adolescents have not been found to be a particularly tortured segment of society, at war with parents. Barnes, summarising from a selection of the research, says:

> *Interviews with over eleven thousand 16 year olds throughout England and Wales found that 89 per cent of boys and 87 per cent of girls said that they got on well with their mothers, and 74 per cent of the boys and 80 per cent of the girls that they got on well with their fathers ... (Ghodsian and Lambert, 1978, National Child Development Study)*

> *... about three quarters of US families are reported to enjoy warm and pleasant relations during the adolescent years and the great majority of teenagers say they admire their parents, feel loved and appreciated by them and are reassured that they can turn to them for advice (Steinberg, 1990) ...*

> *Montemayor (1983) ... estimates that typically, parents and teenagers quarrel about twice a week whereas husbands and wives do so once a week.*

> *... the Isle of Wight study (Rutter et al., 1970, 1976) ... indicated that half of the 14 year olds who withdrew from the family were behaving in a similar fashion earlier in their childhood.*

> *... in only one in ten families is there a dramatic deterioration in parent–child relationships during adolescence (Steinberg, 1990).*

> *(Barnes, 1995, pp. 317–8)*

In the light of evidence of this kind, and research of their own, Coleman and Hendry have argued that although adolescents *do* have to achieve a lot of change, it tends to take place gradually over a period of years, not in a dramatic revolution.

> *In any one day a teenager may choose to confront a parent over the breakfast table, to argue with a sibling, to accept the suggestion of a best friend, to stand up to an authoritarian teacher, to conform to peer group pressure ... We believe that most young people pace themselves through the adolescent transition. Most of them hold back on one issue while they are grappling with another.*

> *(Coleman and Hendry, 1990, pp. 213–4)*

So it seems that the popular view of adolescence as a time of intense crisis in one's self and in the family may be greatly exaggerated. Obviously the adolescents who came to Erikson's psychiatric clinic would not have been typical of adolescents in general. While his account might be very helpful in understanding young people recognised as having serious problems, we clearly need to be very careful about generalising Erikson's insights to *all* adolescents.

There have also been criticisms of the idea that lives divide up neatly into stages. Giddens argues that ideas about adult life stages are no longer workable (1991). He says that modern society is continually changing and that life has become increasingly fluid. It is no longer any help to draw on traditional ideas or the experiences of previous generations. We have to work out our identities for ourselves as we go along. People are in and out of jobs, move to new places, leave partners and take up with new ones, travel all over the world for their holidays and stay in touch with the wide world through the mass media.

Erikson, and Giddens for that matter, stress the importance of an identity which is constructed or maintained by the self. But identity is also something which may be conferred. In Unit 12 you looked at the ways racial stereotyping and discriminatory acts limit and deny opportunities to certain groups in society. You'll remember Lynthia Grant pointing out how stereotypes about black men's roles as fathers affect their own understanding of how to be a father, undermining their self-confidence.

Such behaviour draws on particular forms of social identity conferred by others and sustained through attitudes and assumptions as well as actions. The acquisition of certain social identities, for example becoming known as a carer, may have more positive outcomes, particularly if this means that you become recognised as being entitled to financial support. Social identities may therefore be welcome or unwelcome, and of course most people are not restricted to only one at a time. In the Reader in Chapter 5 Tom Heller talks about himself not only as a GP, but as a father, husband, colleague and potential 'tearaway' and 'voyeur'. People acquire different social identities throughout their lives, with old age as perhaps the final and most powerfully determining identity of all.

So we must be careful not to accept Erikson's ideas uncritically. Yet we can still find use for them. He helps us, for example, to answer my earlier question 'Why is identity important?' Talking of his work with disturbed war-time soldiers he wrote of '... the loss in these men of a sense of identity ... as if, subjectively, their lives no longer hung together – and never would again' (Erikson, 1977, p. 36). Elsewhere he says '... in the social jungle of human existence there is no feeling of being alive without a sense of identity' (Erikson, 1968, p. 130). And as we see from his account of his eight stages, without an adequate sense of identity we are, he believes, exposed to a basic lack of trust and hope; to a sense of shame, guilt, inadequacy and confusion; and later in life to isolation, stagnation and despair.

Study skills: Reading about theories

Does the Erikson piece seem different from the general run of reading in the course? If so, how? One difference is that many of the K100 readings are accounts of research into, or people's experiences of, aspects of care services and practice – whereas, what Erikson is presenting here is *theory*. (The Goffman pieces you read were also theory.) What does that mean – and what differences does it make to your reading?

What you have here is an attempt by Erikson to *explain* part of the psychological process of 'growing up'. He isn't claiming that what he says is definitely 'true'. He is offering us a way to make sense of some complicated and hidden processes of development. You are not meant to read this as 'information' to 'memorise'. These are *ideas* for you to think about *critically*. Criticising a theory does not mean simply 'attacking'. It means weighing up carefully and comparing with other ways of explaining. How do you do that? You may feel that you haven't much else to compare with just yet. It's something that comes with practice, as you get deeper into the subject. However, one thing you *can* do is try to apply Erikson's ideas to the real world and see how well they fit. Think about some children you know (or have known in the past), or cast back to your own childhood experiences. Can you think of examples of the kinds of actions and emotions that Erikson is talking about? Does his account seem to make any sense in terms of your own experience of the world? Are there aspects which don't seem to fit? Note them down.

Your own experience can't *prove* Erikson's case one way or the other, but it can help you begin trying out how useful the ideas seem to be. Beyond that, we can tell you that Erikson was writing within a particular tradition of thought. He was a practising psychoanalyst, building his ideas from those of the founding father of psychoanalysis, Sigmund Freud. So his approach tends to be particularly relevant to understanding the problems of young people who are thought to be in some way disturbed. Later in the unit, we consider some criticisms of Erikson's approach. This does not mean that Erikson is wrong and his critics are right. *All* theories can be criticised. Indeed they *should* be. That is how knowledge advances.

We all plan our daily actions by using theories to make sense of what is going on around us (theories about how relationships work, about buses coming in pairs, about the weather). We can never be absolutely sure of any theory – we simply use the best we can find. Erikson's is a theory that has been widely used to understand the way people develop 'identities'. Other theories build from different starting points. When you are trying to understand a particular problem it can be helpful to try out different theories, to see what insight each can offer. In fact you will find that essay questions sometimes ask you to compare how different theories would approach a particular issue.

You will get used to weighing up and trying out different theories as you advance in your studies. For now the point is to recognise that you are neither meant to *accept as true* every argument you read nor to *abandon* every theory that is criticised. But you should read 'critically' – asking questions and looking for alternative explanations. In higher level studies you learn to live with uncertainty – accepting that knowledge is something that we 'make' and keep on making.

You've spent some time looking at a particular theory of identity development. How might we try to apply this to someone's actual experience? Let's just pause for a moment and think about Jamie Knight in the light of Erikson's ideas. It's possible that social workers like Sarah Burrows are familiar with Erikson's model when they are working with a young person like Jamie. It might help to alert them to some of the problems he could be experiencing.

Thinking back to how Jamie described his early years, would he have been able to develop any sense of basic trust in his first year? He mentioned his father frequently beating him. How would that have helped him to develop a sense of autonomy? As he moved between different homes did he have difficulty developing a consistent idea of right and wrong? And how did he pull everything together in adolescence as he developed his adult identity? He sounds different now from the 'angry little boy' that Sarah described. Perhaps the time spent making his life story book has been a helpful part of the whole process of the development of meaningful identity in his life now that he's able to work on his own commitments with his girlfriend and his daughter.

Key points

- Our identity gives us our sense of meaning in life.
- Erikson's eight stages of development are one way of explaining how identity develops throughout life, from infancy to old age.
- Criticisms of Erikson's model focus on the ways in which life is much less fixed and determined than he allows for.
- A theory like Erikson's can be helpful in providing a set of reference points for the descriptions people give of their life experience.

Section 4
Identity as resource

We've looked at ways in which children and young people can make use of life story books to manage transitions in their lives – reconstructing lost identities and incorporating memories and experiences from the past into their present identity. Now we're going on to look at how past identities can be drawn on to serve changing needs in an individual.

In Unit 4 we spent some time considering how 'social reality' comes to be constructed through everyday events, producing particular kinds of patterns of social interactions that people recognise and so are able to respond to. These ideas have been developed in some detail by the sociologist Erving Goffman (1971). We're going to use these ideas to focus on a particular situation which may be familiar to you, the experience of illness. You'll remember from Unit 2 and your reading of Pinder in the Reader (Chapter 13) how chronic illness is experienced and how people with Parkinson's disease in particular were strongly motivated to gain control over their lives.

Our interest here is in the experience of chronic illness, not only in terms of its characteristics and impact on people's lives, but also in terms of how ill people are seen by carers and how their own identity or past identities make a contribution to the way the illness is coped with or managed.

When someone is ill, they are not only affected by the illness itself, they also learn *how* to be ill in such a way that they can be recognised as an ill person and therefore get help, or help themselves. They acquire an identity as an ill person, or behave according to a 'sick role' (Stacey, 1988, p. 196)

Activity 8   **Taking on the sick role**

Allow a few minutes   You might like to try out the idea of the 'sick role' by drawing on your own experience of being ill. Jot down a few words about what happened. How did people know you were ill? Did it mean you had to change your plans? Did you seek advice on what to do? Did you feel other people understood that you were ill? Did you get the help and support you needed?

Comment   Not everyone accepts the sick role. Perhaps you're the sort of person who feels you have to keep going and not give in to the illness. Does that mean you were rejecting the idea of being ill, or did you really not have time to be ill? Some people accept being sick as a way of escaping from other people or things they don't want to do, a kind of space in their lives to dwell on themselves. For other people, being ill is a threat to their identity. They find it difficult to ask for or accept help from someone else. And then there are the social conventions which may mean that you are not expected to take part in activity. You may feel marginalised and excluded, however well-meaning your family and friends are. People may bring you fruit and flowers, confirming your ill identity and this may come as something of a shock. There may be sympathetic cards from colleagues. You may feel in a quandary. If I'm too ill to go to work am I too ill to go out for the evening?

However you felt about being ill you probably found that once you had decided you were ill then things changed, like staying in bed and being allowed to miss appointments, things being reorganised without you, getting attention from a doctor.

Some kinds of illness draw attention to the future not just present states. The US sociologist Talcott Parsons coined the term 'the sick role'. He argued that behaviour can only be understood in terms of the meanings of the people and things with which a person, or a group or organisation is in contact. This includes not only the people being interacted with and their reactions in turn, but also the physical situation, the signs and symbols which people use and the rules, norms and values which 'guide' or control behaviour (Rocher, 1972, pp. 28–31). His particular interest was in this last set of influences so that when people are ill, or 'sick' , they behave in ways which are expected of ill people. Parsons' idea is an interesting one. When we are ill we are not only affected by the nature of the illness itself, he suggests we learn *how* to be ill in such a way that we can be recognised as being ill and therefore be helped, or help ourselves. We adopt a role, a set of behaviours, that other people recognise and join in with.

The 'sick role' may have long-term consequences for identity. In Unit 2 you also looked at the difference between acute and chronic illness. A member of our course team who has diabetes responded to Activity 8 by pointing out that:

> *I feel very different knowing I have to live with a chronic condition than when I just have a cold. It's to do with managing the here and now but also being conscious of disability at some point. I sometimes try to prepare myself for something which may happen, for example losing a limb or losing my sight.*

A chronic illness or condition has a way of taking over someone's identity. This may be because of its outward signs, or it may be because it limits or restricts the way someone is able to interact with others. It may be because the illness and understanding and managing it becomes a full-time concern. All these aspects of the 'sick role' have implications for how someone is regarded and the meanings that the illness develops for them in their life.

Even though the impact of illness may mean that an identity may be changed and the 'sick role' takes over there are reasons for maintaining a broader view. Someone who has diabetes is not only 'a diabetic' just as someone admitted to casualty doesn't immediately lose their name and become 'the fractured femur'. The idea of the 'sick role' is helpful in pointing out how illness and being ill can be observed as a social as much as a medical condition, but does it also distract attention away from the whole person with a lifetime of experience? To explore some of these and other issues we're going to listen to Paul Theobald talking about living with AIDS.

Paul Theobald was 50 when he was interviewed for K100 about his life and more recent experience of being HIV positive. Paul is a member of the Council of Management of London Lighthouse, a residential and support centre for men and women affected by HIV and AIDS. Paul has had an eventful life. He was given up for adoption at the age of three months and only met his mother again in his early 30s when he traced her in Canada. He was adopted into a family which broke up when he was 14. However, he is still in close touch with his adopted sisters. He later joined the army, left, went to India on the 'hippy trail' and then

The other Lib group on the march today

GAY IS ANGRY, read the inscriptions on the Harley Street pavement, puzzling many an honest citizen. Gay in this case means homosexual, and homosexuals are angry with the psychiatrists who describe homosexuality as a sickness and undertake to cure it.

"Go away and take these pills," mimics Jonathan Wild, at the headquarters of the Gay Liberation Front in King's Cross, "and come back in six weeks. And if you're still feeling queer, then it's shock therapy for you."

The GLF are an alliance of some 300 homosexuals, male and female. Today they are holding a Gay Day picnic at Speaker's Corner, followed by a rally in Trafalgar Square

They are united in a desire to remove the stigma from homosexuality, and in the case of having a sexual liaison with a man under 21, the fear of prosecution and imprisonment.

Their headquarters are a basement room in a bookshop. Gay Liberation Against Aversion Therapy, runs the sign on the wall. A letter asks for recruits for a Jewish homosexual society.

"Maybe 33 per cent of people are bisexual," explains Jonathan Wild. "We are convincing people of the need to express their bisexuality," says a young man called Bob, another member of the "office commune" which runs things. "Because of the way people are conditioned and repress their homosexuality, it means for many of them either a very poor sex life, or no sex life at all."

Homosexual men and women, say the GLF, are continually harassed and discriminated against.

"Maybe it's getting better," says Jonathan, "but very slowly. You are conditioned so much to the Man/Woman thing. And if a kid decides he is not going to make it with a woman and wants to make it with a man, he is made to feel guilty and ashamed."

"Lots of people are having a bad time mentally, living a double life," says Bob.

GLF is trying to make people proud of homosexuality, saying that being gay is maybe better than being straight, and not something to be done furtively, on the weekend.

The Front has run into a little

THE GAY LIBERATION FRONT—the society which fights for the recognition and the rights of homosexuals, both men and women, is staging a march today in London. STAN GEBLER DAVIES spoke to some of the GLF members to find out more about Gay Lib's aims and ideas . . .

discrimination itself. There was difficulty getting an office and a place to hold meetings. The GLF started last October, inspired by the American example. They hold meetings every Wednesday evening in All Saints Church hall in Notting Hill Gate. Most of the members adjourn, as usual with political meetings, to a pub afterwards. "We ran into trouble there.

A few couples were kissing and the manager came up and said, get out. We said why? We're not doing anything that other couples are not doing, except they happen to be heterosexual. He wouldn't listen."

The freedom to kiss and hold hands in public may not seem very precious, but the GLF see it as a perfectly reasonable thing to ask. Twenty-five per cent of their membership, incidentally, is female.

They have taken their plea for toleration into the East End as well as Notting Hill Gate and the purlieus of the Underground.

The reception was better than they might have expected. They found a great many working-class people talking sympathetically to them, once they got over the shock of discovering how "normal" they looked.

"We went out among the mums and dads and kids in Victoria Park," says Jonathan, "and they were surprised to speak to us because we aren't like the stereotype. We looked just like them and talked just like them. Some of them, particularly the older ones, said we were the type who molested little children outside the gates of primary schools. But they wouldn't believe that sort of crap if the media hadn't twisted it."

Picture Frank Tewkesbury.

Paul Theobald in the early days of Gay Liberation (London Evening Standard, *28 August 1971*)

came back to England. By this time he realised that he was gay and became involved in the 1970s gay rights movement in London, as well as getting into prostitution, drug use and drug dealing. He took a decision to make a change in his life in 1979 when he moved to the USA, which is where we pick up his story on the tape.

Paul Theobald. This photograph was taken when he joined the Council of Management of London Lighthouse

Activity 9   Identity and illness

Allow about 1 hour   The interview with Paul Theobald on Audio Cassette 4 side 2 lasts 25
    minutes and you may want to listen to it more than once. In the Offprints
Book you'll find an account of how AIDS develops (Offprint 20). If you
aren't familiar with the disease you may find it helpful to read through the
article after you've listened to Paul talking because he uses some medical
terms. Like some of the people with Parkinson's disease interviewed by
Ruth Pinder, he has expert knowledge about his condition.

(a)   See if you can pick out the different identities which Paul mentions as
he talks about his life over the last 20 years.

(b)   How do these contribute to the way he manages his illness?

Comment   (a)   **Different identities**

Paul begins by describing how people in the gay community of New
York first began to realise that they were being affected by a new
kind of illness: 'HIV started to come into the community about '82'
and 'it did only seem to be affecting the <u>gay community</u>'. As a <u>gay
man</u> he was part of that community and shared aspects of its
lifestyle. He talks about 'we' when he remembers being frightened by
what was happening. He also mentions a particular newspaper article
by Larry Kramer, a leading campaigner for gay rights, at a time when
the disease was still called GRID or 'gay related immune deficiency'
(Van der Vliet, 1996, p. 66).

Listening to Paul's memories of that time we hear him talking about
himself as a <u>gay rights activist</u> who was keen to get involved in a
health campaign. The result was that he became <u>a volunteer</u> at an
organisation in New York called Gay Men's Health Crisis. He next
became a <u>part-time social worker</u> and later the <u>manager</u> of a
supported housing programme at an AIDS resource centre. He was
also a <u>volunteer</u> who took part in early health studies of gay men and
this was how he found out he was <u>HIV positive</u>. Back in England, as
well as working with people with drug and alcohol problems, he
helped set up a <u>self-help</u> group and not long after that he was
<u>diagnosed</u> as having AIDS. He talks about meeting other people with
AIDS and identifying with them. He's a <u>50-year-old man</u> and a '<u>hippy
sixties era kind of person with HIV</u>'. He's a <u>recovered drug addict</u>.

I've underlined just some of the ways I noticed Paul talks about
himself. You may have noticed others. For example he mentions his
'spiritual kind of search' and his 'experiences of living with the virus'.
These both suggest ways of being and relating to other people.

(b)   **Managing his illness**

It seems as if Paul brings a great deal of his past life and experience
to managing his illness. He's a campaigner who became aware of
issues around HIV at an early point. From this he's learnt the
importance of working with other people and sharing information and
support. He's someone who has an awareness of the impact which a
long-term illness can have on life. He's known about HIV for nearly
15 years and he's worked with other people who became ill and died.
This seemed to give him the idea that he might not develop AIDS.
More recently the development of symptoms has made him realise
that particular identity was not to be his. He says 'It threw me into a
loop when I got my diagnosis'. In dealing with that blow, he says
being a recovered drug addict helps. He comes over as someone
who has a strong sense of the need to manage and control his life.

Now he's focusing on how to cope with being ill most of the time. He says 'I already had a few lives' so it seems that it's important to him now to be able to reflect on and remember his past. Talking about dying he's certain that he wants the people who care for him to know 'the fullness of my life'. Perhaps most important to him is being a gay man who is part of a generation and a strongly identified group which gives him support and inspiration.

Having listened to Paul talking about himself and the many different experiences he draws on in dealing with his illness you may like to contrast the way he talks about himself and his illness with the approach implicit in the biomedical model which was discussed in Unit 2. His account focuses our attention not just on the illness but more broadly on the whole person, his life and what this brings to his understanding of his own condition as well as other people's through his work as a volunteer at London Lighthouse.

He's come to terms with the limits which the illness has set on his life in terms of working and socialising and an end which may come sooner than he had expected. But there are continuities with earlier parts of his life, as he points out. He has been able to go on working, unpaid, and this is important to him. He knows where to get help, in the medical sense, but also socially, emotionally and spiritually. As a member of a doubly stigmatised group – a gay man with AIDS – he draws on the strength of shared identities and experiences to reaffirm the particular choices he has made during his life. Knowing something about Paul Theobald's past may help his carers and supporters to understand him better and, as he also points out, by drawing on his own earlier life, past identities become a resource for him in his present situation. Parsons's concept of the 'sick role' may be a useful tool to help us understand that there is a set of behaviours associated with being ill; however, an account like Paul Theobald's helps us to see how much someone may bring to that 'sick role' from their earlier life and current relationships and associations.

Paul's concern about preparing for death might be seen as pushing him prematurely into old age: Erikson's stage of 'ego integrity v. despair'. As Paul explains, 'Those of us who are faced with a life threatening illness … have the opportunity to … deal with some issues that most people aren't sort of encouraged to deal with until they're very old'. Carers, who may be friends, family, or professionals like social workers or nurses, need to be aware of the active role which someone like Paul can play in making decisions and expressing his individuality at all stages of his illness. Being aware of his life story is a part of the process of guaranteeing a 'whole person' approach to his care and support.

Key points

- Being ill is a form of behaviour – when people are ill they act in ways which help to confirm that they are ill. Such activity is helpful to the ill person and those trying to help them – they develop an identity as an ill person.

- Someone's identity as an ill person is only one among many identities which are meaningful to them and to other people close to them.

- Having a terminal illness may mean that someone is being pushed into Erikson's final stage of life at a relatively young age. Opportunities to talk and reflect about a past life may be helpful.

- Bringing an understanding of aspects of pre-existing identities to illness can improve the quality of help and support offered.

Section 5
Remembering in old age

In this section we focus specifically on remembering in old age and look at ways to maintain and renew identity at the end of life, sometimes when people are experiencing an accumulation of adversity.

5.1 Identity in late life

So far in this unit you've looked at how references to the past can be a way to establish self-identity. Recalling the past is also a means of establishing *social* identity. In conversation people draw on shared understandings of music, films, games, jokes and stories which is a way of establishing who they are, what they know and what they've done with their lives. In different situations people show more or less of themselves, depending on how they feel or what seems to be appropriate. Sometimes there is a choice about this, but at other times it feels as if there isn't. The answers I might give to a telephone market researcher may give a false impression of who I think I am: 'No I don't own a car' (but I can drive, I just choose not to most of the time).

Home as a source for identity

Family, friends, workmates and neighbours help to bolster up who you are. We saw in Unit 7 how in their own homes people surround themselves with things that are important to them: ornaments, photographs, furniture, plants, even pets in their different ways convey messages. But what happens when you are lifted out of that environment, or if circumstances change; how do people know who you are without all these cues around you? Even when someone is still living in their own home what happens when they are the only survivor from their family and friends? Who helps to maintain identity then?

Back in Unit 7, Activity 11 asked you to list eight things which you would take with you if you had to move to a place with limited space. You may have found that quite a difficult list to make. It's an exercise which is often used in training sessions when younger people are being helped to identify with the feelings of much older people who are going through the kind of loss associated with relocation. One of our testers remembered that this was a particularly difficult experience: 'This is what my mother-in-law had to do. Very painful for her'.

Workers in health and social care may meet people on a fairly frequent basis but even then they may know very little about them and their past lives. David Widgery, a GP in the East End of London, wrote about one of his patients, Mr Foley:

> *Although a docker, Mr Foley had always been a little man. He was devoted to his rosy-cheeked, smiling, neatly made-up, welcoming wife. Their flat was in apple-pie order and he always attended on time for his blood pressure checks. Except one day when she, apologetically, called to cancel his appointment and asked me to visit myself. 'He's poorly today', she said with a special tone. He was. Somehow exuding a new weakness, and welcoming me with an expression I had never seen on his kindly face before: a slight, beseeching look, half gratitude, half fear. I made to examine him with much jocular opening of my medical bag and reassuring brandishing of the stethoscope to give myself time to observe him. He had suddenly become bird-like: wrists tiny, cheekbones hollowed out, skin translucent. He has always been petite but now, only six weeks after I had last seen him, he had begun to be emaciated.*

> *[David Widgery diagnoses correctly that Mr Foley has advanced cancer of the lung.]*

> *Only two weeks later he died. At home. Sooner than I or anyone had expected. The district nurses were marvellous, finding sheepskins for his bedsore and book rests and high-calorie drinks. In that short time, I got to know Mr Foley as I had never done before: learnt about his singing down at the club, dressing up at parties, his sense of humour, the family's pride in the Foley brothers' record for staunch trade unionism in the Docks.*

> *(Widgery, 1991, pp. 136–7)*

Dr Widgery with a patient at home in Bow, London

Dr Widgery felt that he only got to know who his patient really was as he was dying. You may feel that this is inevitable, given case loads, a market-driven world and the need to focus on someone's immediate need for health care. But how can appropriate help and support be developed if all that is known is their details as a patient, client or service user? There is research evidence which suggests that with opportunities to know more about the life histories of their patients, nurses, for example, develop more positive attitudes and greater sensitivity towards their older patients (Pietrukowicz and Johnson, 1991). You might like to think back to Unit 4 where some issues of power in nursing settings were discussed. In a study on a continuing care ward Evers suggested that auxiliary nurses chose not to talk about the lifelong informal caring skills of their women patients in order to assert their own professional status (1981, p. 126). The issue about what is known and what is told to whom under what conditions about the personal lives of service users is a recurrent theme in K100 and you'll find it discussed again in some of the later units.

Keeping in contact with all those parts of your life which give you your identity can sometimes feel difficult when you're growing old in a country, or even an area which is far from where you grew up. One older man from the Caribbean pointed out to some researchers that:

> *People cannot reminisce here in Britain which is very important. I feel it's taken people a long time to decide to go home, because as they are getting older it's about reminiscences. When you are young you are saying that you are making plans. After saying when are we going to go home, by the time I reach 60 I will revert back to talk about family history and the importance of childhood in the Caribbean, you cannot have those reminiscences in an old people's home in this country. The people in these homes never talk to you. People are not going to listen to you.*

> (Plaza, 1996, p. 16)

A Bangladeshi woman's account explains why identity maintenance can sometimes be difficult:

> *My father-in-law died a year and a half after I came here. We sent his body back home. But none of us was able to accompany the body. At that time my husband and my brother-in-law both had full-time three shift jobs with British Steel. They couldn't get leave and the dead body had to go alone. But in Bangladesh our relatives came to the airport and they took the body back to our village home. They buried him in the village. My mother-in-law became very frail after my father-in-law died, so we didn't let her go back. My mother-in-law is now seventy. She always stays at home now. It's difficult for her to move about outside the house and the cold affects her quite badly. My sister-in-law lives here. We also have a few other close relatives in England. So for this reason we didn't send my mother-in-law back to Bangladesh. And she too doesn't want to travel there by herself leaving us behind in this country. My brother-in-law's wife and I now live in separate houses. My mother-in-law lives with me for a while and with my brother-in-law's wife for a while. We want her to stay here with us in loving comfort.*

> (Ara and Chatterjee, 1995, pp. 19–20)

Asian family newly arrived in Bradford c. 1960s. Do their symbols of material success indicate new identities?

Activity 10 **When did you last ...?**

Allow about 5 minutes The elderly African-Caribbean man in the quote above was talking as if he expects to reminisce more about his childhood as he grows older. Is that your experience? When did you last find yourself talking about things you remember doing when you were younger? Was it at a family gathering, with friends, or at an office party? Did you find you learnt something new about people you thought you already knew quite well? Were you able to find someone to share your memories or did you feel cut off by your own experience? Pause for a moment and think about your own habits of remembering.

Comment Identity is very much expressed through behaviour, what we do in life. For some older people, the loss of a meaningful role may feel extremely damaging to a sense of identity. In a society where compulsory retirement at earlier and earlier ages removes older people from paid work and in which rapid technological change and the short-term philosophy of the free market seems to place a sell-by date on most forms of knowledge, older people may sense a lack of role or contribution. Interestingly, what may feel like uncertainty about what being old is about is happening at a time when the proportion of older people in the richer part of the world has never been greater. Some researchers argue that older people have a biological role in human society helping to contribute towards its welfare and survival with their long memories and their ability to pass on experience and moral values through stories and myths. One contribution which older people may be making when they reminisce is to pass on their experience of life and history to succeeding generations. In this way, reminiscence is a central core in the identity of older people (Coleman, 1993, pp. 19–20).

A tester who read through this activity had quite a hostile reaction to the last point:

> *Isn't it just this that puts younger generations off? Hearing my Dad go over his version of key events endlessly is a terrible burden and **not** enlightenment, though worse is the perpetual rehearsal of how much the chocolate cost on the station at Ulverston or how many pairs of socks got wet on his 1937 cycle trip to Scotland. Memories!!! Who needs them!?*

This last and somewhat lively point raises a number of issues which we'll be looking at in greater depth in what follows. Who listens and what they do with what they hear is perhaps as important as the recall and reminiscing itself. Someone interested in the history of cycling might be delighted to hear so much detail from 60 years ago, but it's different for the family member who has been hearing these stories for 50 years. And of course, not being able to forget can also be a great burden, as the US broadcaster and oral historian Studs Terkel describes:

> *But a memory like that's a curse too, because it means I remember things I don't **want** to remember, things I'd sooner forget. Incidents I'm not too proud of, that I'd sooner pretend hadn't happened, I can't wipe them out of my mind. That's the downside of it, that's what goes with having a retentive memory, the price you have to pay for it.*
>
> *(Quoted in Parker, 1997, p. 210)*

5.2 Legitimising remembering

It may seem surprising but not all that long ago people working as carers were advised to discourage older people from reminiscing about the past. Robert Butler, a psychogeriatrician working in the US in the early 1960s, had been observing older people living independently in the community. He argued that life review is a:

> *... naturally occurring, universal mental process characterised by the progressive return to consciousness of past experiences, and particularly, the resurgence of unresolved conflicts.*
>
> *(Butler, 1963, p. 66)*

Butler's ideas had a major impact on a generation of carers working with older people in residential, day care and nursing settings.

Activity 11   **A watershed article**

Allow about 20 minutes   Turn to Chapter 16 in the Reader and read through as far as the paragraph ending with the reference to Erikson.

Note down some of the conflicts which older people's reminiscing raised for staff before and after the impact of Butler's article was felt in care settings. Do you think that these issues have been resolved today?

Comment Rose Dobroff mentions the conflict staff experienced who did not 'feel free' to listen to the stories which older people told them. She describes this dramatically as a liberating moment. But then she mentions how talking also meant painful memories were recalled. Though she says that remembering, reminiscing, could be helpful, it ultimately could not resolve the pain. These are issues which remain today, as we shall go on to see.

Claims about the helpfulness of reminiscence and recall have been subjected to much investigation and some criticism. One particularly important piece of research seems to suggest that it is important to be aware that remembering the past is not something that all older people do equally or for the same reasons.

Activity 12 **How older people feel about reminiscing**

Allow about 15 minutes

Go back to Chapter 16 in the Reader and work through to the end. When you have finished look back at Coleman's table of 'Attitudes to reminiscence and related morale'. What do you think was so different about Coleman's approach to finding out about reminiscence in comparison with that of other researchers?

Comment Coleman listened to a group of older people over a period of years in what is called a 'longitudinal study'. This meant that he was able to hear people talking over a period of time, several years in fact. He also chose to listen to what they had to say in a reasonably natural way, instead of being prompted and answers measured under more experimental conditions. He was interested in how people felt about remembering, so he also asked them questions about that. He was not just interested in listening to people talk about the past, he wanted to know how they felt about the present too. As we've already seen, talk about the past is as much about who we feel we are now as who we think we were then. Finally, the way he chose to find out meant that he was able to identify two groups of people who did *not* reminisce – a high morale group who did not feel that the past was important to them in their present state, and a low morale group who avoided talk about the past because it was too painful.

Reminiscence has been seen as a panacea for many things, and a source of happiness and satisfaction. This may not always be the case. And, just as practitioners and carers at an earlier stage knew from the older people they worked with that remembering is an activity that should be responded to and not prevented, it is also the case that care staff and others are aware that for some people remembering past events is not always a positive experience. Coleman's work serves to keep a balance between enthusiasm and sensitive awareness.

> **Key points**
>
> • Reminiscing is a normal part of human mental activity at any stage of life.
>
> • Sometimes identities in late life can become hidden or obscured if surroundings change or someone is a lone survivor.
>
> • Opportunities to talk about the past can be helpful to some people in old age.
>
> • Not everyone will need or want to be encouraged to talk about the past.
>
> • Life experience will vary – it's important to find ways of supporting people in ways that are individual to them or which relate to their particular culture or background.

5.3 Traumatic memories

In Britain the 50th anniversary of VE Day and revellings in nostalgic wartime fashion, songs, food and films seemed to bring back warm memories of sharing, comradeship and victorious survival. However, some psychologists were concerned that this celebratory remembering would stir up painful memories among those who had not found ways to deal with distressing wartime experiences. Fifty years on some older men were saying that they were haunted by war memories every day. Images of the war in Bosnia had made matters worse. For example, one man who had been imprisoned by the Japanese army in Singapore's Changi camp found that feelings of grief and anger were reawakened by pictures of starving men surrounded by barbed wire in Bosnia (Mihill, 1995).

What these men were experiencing has quite recently been named as 'post traumatic stress disorder'. In the First World War it was known as 'shell shock'. Similar symptoms were seen among veterans of the Falklands and Gulf Wars, among the survivors of major accidents such as the sinking of the Herald of Free Enterprise, and among survivors of torture, abuse, bombings or natural disasters like floods and fire. Psychologists who work with survivors of disasters now believe that stress can be dealt with if people are helped to discuss their feelings near the time, or are able to revisit places such as prison camps, battlefields and disaster areas. War veterans who were not offered support or understanding at the time, or who were encouraged to hide their feelings and to find distraction in work, were facing problems in retirement. Late in life, the opportunity to talk and be in touch with others who had shared similar experiences helped reduce the distress of the men who had been prisoners of war in the Far East. Talking about the trauma of racism faced by black Second World War veterans whose patriotism brought them to fight in Europe, only to find they were rejected as civilians in post-war Britain, is helpful in today's Britain where their part in the war effort tends to be overlooked (Bousquet and Douglas, 1991; Murray, 1996).

Workers interested in developing reminiscence-based activities with any age group are often concerned that they may stir up painful memories and powerful emotions. Coleman's research showed, and everyday

West Indian aircraftsmen, whose recruitment was vetoed by the War Office until 1943

'We fought everywhere for one reason – patriotism.'

As D-Day peace breaks out West Indians issue reminder of their part in the war which claimed 20,000 lives from Caribbean

'Forgotten' veterans raise glasses of rum pu...

John Mullin

They were the forgotten soldiers of war, and Connie Goodridge-Mark, aged 71, wanted to look just right. "Hold on a minute. A girl's got to look her best," she said, pulling a blood red lipstick from her bag.

At the operational HQ of the West Indian Ex-Servicemen and Women's Association in Clapham, south London, attention was drawn to a little-known fact: West Indians played an important role in the war effort. As many as 20,000 people from the Caribbean died during the second world war.

As veterans' leaders emerged from the National Heritage Department yesterday after a meeting which appeared to have ended the controversy over the Government's plans to mark the 50th anniversary of the Normandy landings, West Indian army, navy and airforce veterans were launching a battle in Clapham to raise their profile.

But their Lest We Forget exhibition was no po-faced affair. "Fancy a rum punch?" asked Rene Webb, aged 73, the chairman.

There had been a bar on black recruits in the West Indies until 1943. The Colonial Office had wanted to allow West Indians to join the war effort, but the War Office fought the move. Major General Arthur Dowler,

(*Guardian*, 28 April 1994)

one of the army officers responsible, argued: "While there are many coloured men of high mentality and cultural distinction, the generality are of a simple mental outlook. They work hard when they have no money, and when they have money, prefer to do nothing until it's gone."

People from the Caribbean suspended their swelling opposition to colonialism when the war began. There were 8,000 in the RAF alone. "We fought everywhere: in Africa and in Europe. There was one reason: patriotism," said Hector Watson, aged 68, who was a transport driver in Britain with the RAF.

Mrs Goodridge-Mark worked for the British effort in Jamaica, and came to Britain in 1954 with her cricketer husband.

The Caribbean was strategically vital to the Germans, who wanted to control traffic between the Atlantic and Pacific oceans through the Panama Canal. There was even an internment camp on Jamaica. "I remember taking letters to my boss's office, and where was a German POW there, cleaning. He grabbed me and gave me the biggest kiss I had ever had in my life. Then ...

The survivors enjo... war days. Cecil Ho... 71, was a mechani... RAF. He arrived i... for training three ... D-Day. But it was... story for those wh... after the war.

"Accommodation... hard to find. I re... calling up one lady who had advertised. "When she came to the door, she took a step back in... She... late ... take... telep... road... I rang... been ... you.'... you k... that pe... involve... for our... Veteran... their m... they we... assuran... meeting... Departm... proposal... event in ... Les Frost... Veterans... "We have... of agreem...

Express yourself: survivors of chilhood sexual abuse do not want their pain to be swept under the carpet

(*Community Care*, 28 March 1996)

observation tells us, that remembering may not be a welcome activity for some people. It may be troubling and may evoke emotions which are difficult to deal with. Workers or carers who feel that they do not have the skills necessary to help should be able to identify where they, or the person who is distressed, can get help. This means knowing how to find or take steps to refer someone to appropriate professional help such as specialist counsellors, doctors and qualified psychotherapists. We'll be returning to this issue in Unit 15 when we discuss group work.

One group of people whose harrowing memories have come to be seen as important to a complete record of the past are survivors of the Holocaust. Though the story of how six million Jews were murdered during the Second World War might now be considered as well known, particularly following the impact of the film 'Schindler's List', it seems that older Jewish people, especially those whose families were murdered, still find it difficult to talk about their experiences or to find people who are ready to listen.

Activity 13   **When talking about the past is difficult**

Allow about 10 minutes   Pause for a moment and write down a few ideas you may have as to why people who have experienced traumatic and difficult events find it difficult to talk about them.

Comment   You may have identified some of the same reasons that I list below:

How to put it into words. Sometimes people who have suffered traumatic experiences simply cannot find the right words to explain what has happened to them.

Not being believed. They may fear that they won't be believed because their story sounds so extraordinary.

Feelings of guilt. There may be a problem with feelings of guilt for being one of the few survivors of an ordeal.

Feelings of suspicion. There may be a fear that in order to survive they might be suspected of having behaved selfishly.

Is there anything more to be said? It might be supposed that accounts of, say, the Jewish Holocaust or child sexual abuse, have been so well publicised that there is nothing new to be said. Someone with painful memories may feel that the story has been well told by others, or that their personal account can add nothing to already highly publicised stories. However, psychologists who work with people who have traumatic memories recognise that even in the case of, for example, the Hillsborough Football Stadium disaster, the ways in which people experience and remember the same event can be highly individual. There will always be a personal story to tell.

Despite the difficulties which people with traumatic memories face, opportunities to talk and share feelings can be helpful. Talking in groups can help people to regain trust and feelings of shared understanding. Traumatic memories become a part of identity. What seems to be important for people with disturbing memories is to be listened to and for their stories and accounts to be recognised and accepted by others.

As well as talking and listening there is the recording of experiences for posterity. Survivors of the Jewish Holocaust feel the need to ensure that their experience should never be repeated. Many have taken part in video recordings, talking to schools and colleges and publishing their experiences in books and collections. Survivors of child abuse similarly have begun to write about their experiences as a means to share and gain understanding for their situation. People who witnessed the Hillsborough disaster in 1989 have also been keen to make sure that others can learn the truth as they experienced it (Taylor and Ward, 1995). To talk may also be a way of 'letting go' of painful memories to start work on a new future. We saw how this could be an important feature in life story work with children and young people.

Ramani uses poetry as a way of telling her story of abuse:

Childhood

Roti and dal
Slither down
My dry throat
Pani to wash it down with
Acrylic and nylon
Cover my skin
Images flicker
On the TV screen
I sit comatosed
Occasionally transferring
To other available islands
Sometimes I dive into books
And sit hidden
Amongst the characters' wordplay
Silent amongst their drama
I nestle craftily behind a settee
Or within the folds of the curtains
Sometimes I perch on top of the lampshade
And watch Little Women, Famous Five or
The Wombles.
Later come Cathy and Jane Eyre.
As I grow older
These childhood escapes
Branch out into more
Elaborate tales and characters.
But I am still there
On the periphery,
Faceless and voiceless.

(Ramani Mundair, in Malone *et al.*, 1996, p. 74)

It's important to emphasise again that for some people, even those who have had traumatic experiences, there may be no wish to reminisce at all. They may have developed an ability to avoid remembering what is painful, as a successful coping strategy. If you look back to Reader Chapter 16 you'll see that Coleman's table shows two groups of people who either avoided thinking about the past, or who saw no point in remembering. In talking about the importance of the past for older people we also have to take note that remembering should be as far as possible a chosen activity.

The issue of the repression of memory and debates about 'false memories' of child abuse has been much debated and discussed. Counsellors and psychotherapists have been accused of stirring up or inducing memories of sexual abuse in clients through suggestion. In the USA there have been court cases where fathers have denied allegations about abusive acts made by grown up children following therapy sessions. In the UK abused children are supported by the organisation

Accuracy about Abuse, while parents and other accused people have formed the British False Memory Society. A survey of therapists who had recently seen someone who had recovered from a traumatic memory found that over a third of such memories did not identify sexual abuse but related to accidents and traumatic medical procedures. Over 40 per cent were able to call up some form of corroborative evidence from other witnesses or outsiders and even confessions from perpetrators (Andrews, 1997). This research has been criticised because it is based on the reports of therapists and does not come directly from those involved in the incidents. Because counsellors and psychotherapists have been seen as being at the centre of the controversy about 'false' or recovered memories, the British Association for Counselling carried out its own review of the literature. The conclusions reached were that:

- many cases of remembering forgotten childhood sexual abuse are straightforward

- amnesia for periods of childhood abuse is possible

- recovery of memories of abuse for which the person has been amnesic is possible.

But

- some practitioners use methods such that no reliance at all could reasonably be placed on what the client tells

- the reality of false memory must be accepted as occurring in at least some cases.

(McGuire, 1997)

Finally, it is important not to underestimate the effect which listening to painful memories can have on the hearer. Counsellors and therapists include in their training skills in sharing their feelings about what they have heard. Care workers may sometimes feel unable to cope with the accounts they hear or they may find memories of their own suffering are stirred up. Carers in these situations should be reassured that they do not have to contain or 'bottle up' any feelings which they also experience. Working with memory and identity means building an environment of care which provides help and support to everyone involved. There may be professionals like social workers or clinical psychologists who can help, or members of groups like foster carers' support groups or networks of survivors of abuse who they can turn to for sympathy and understanding.

Key points

- Some people have experienced traumatic events in their lives. For them, remembering the past may need to be accompanied by identifying appropriate help and support.

- People with traumatic memories need to be assured that someone is prepared to listen to them if this is what they choose.

- Some people may prefer not to talk, they may have developed their own way of coping with past trauma.

- Sometimes workers and carers will also need support if they have been exposed to the painful emotions of others.

Section 6
Identity, memory and dementia

People who experience memory loss due to an illness such as Alzheimer's disease face the possibility of a disappearing identity once they lose the ability to communicate coherently. Mr Bright, who is featured in Unit 7, is fortunate in that his day is spent with people who know him well, his wife and the care staff at Redwood Day Centre. Other people with dementia may face greater difficulties. Tom Kitwood is a researcher into dementia whose approach is to emphasise the importance of maintaining 'personhood' or a sense of the individual self right through the stages of dementing illnesses. Without 'personhood' carers will emphasise only the things which someone cannot achieve, the symptoms of the disease, rather than the identity of the person with the illness. He argues:

> If personhood is to be maintained, it is essential that each individual be appreciated in his or her uniqueness. Where there is empathy without personal knowledge, care will be aimless and unfocused. Where there is personal knowledge without empathy, care will be detached and cold. But when empathy and personal knowledge are brought together, miracles can happen.

> (Kitwood, 1997, p. 39)

People with learning difficulties used to be described in terms of what they couldn't do, their 'weaknesses' or their 'special needs'. In this way individual identity and life history came to be denied or excluded. Similarly, for someone with dementia, once they are isolated in contexts and social situations which are unfamiliar or which place a focus on physical care alone, there is a danger that past identity and skills may be lost or discouraged. Gibson gives an example from her research in Northern Ireland:

> A middle class woman who in residential care spread her scrambled eggs with ham, upended the milk jug into the sugar bowl, drinking the lot. In this home the residents each ate alone in their own bedrooms so there was no one to see except the distressed visiting daughter who lamented her mother's lost competence. When taken out to a hotel for a Sunday lunch, the woman's earlier good manners would reassert themselves in response to the cues and clues she registered from the environment. She would behave impeccably and without embarrassment to anyone, not even the self-conscious teenage grandchildren just waiting to be mortified in public.

> (Gibson, 1991, p. 11)

People with a dementing illness like Alzheimer's disease are often viewed in quite stereotypical ways. The same may be true for anyone lacking verbal communication skills. It may be assumed that they have little awareness of who they are or where they are, and care may be given in a way that denies individuality. Recent research suggests that people with dementia continue to have a sense of self-awareness right up to the later stages of the illness and that they may be only too painfully aware of their own failings. Kitwood (1997) argues that by excluding people from normal social settings and by ignoring the clues they provide as to their feelings and wishes, we help to make them appear more ill than they are.

Faith Gibson argues that although encouraging people with a dementing illness to reminisce cannot help to halt the illness, it can have some positive benefits. Compiling life histories with relatives and listening to what people are actually saying can provide a basis for more sensitive care. It can also help workers to challenge their own attitudes towards particular residents and to believe, rather than to disbelieve what they are told by the person with a dementing illness (Gibson, 1994).

John Killick is someone who brings his skills as a writer to understanding and interpreting people with dementing illnesses.

Activity 14   **Listening and interpreting**

Allow about 20 minutes

Turn to Reader Chapter 15. In this chapter John Killick presents a case for what he calls 'pro-active care'. Being 'pro-active' as he defines it means listening, recording what's said and then taking appropriate action. Read through the chapter and, as you do, note down what you feel each of the people mentioned is communicating about themselves. Do you agree with John Killick's suggestions after each person's account? What difficulties might carers have to overcome to take action?

John Killick practising 'pro-active care'

Comment   Albert Edwards's talk about himself sounds confused. He switches from golf to tea drinking as he puzzles over how he comes to be where he is. He sounds angry with his co-residents and perhaps with his family. Without the opportunity to read through his account he might just come over as someone who tends to go on about tea drinking rather obsessively. Reading through, however, it seems as if talk about tea making is a way of dealing with his past as well as bringing out how he feels about his present situation. It's a constant thread in his life. He sounds like quite an assertive man. Carers may find it difficult to arrive at a balance between risk and autonomy in taking action to resolve some of the issues he's raising.

Jessie Jamieson's past roles as mother and teacher seem to be important to her as well as the places she's lived in. She might find it difficult to concentrate on tasks unless they are things which she's done all her life, chopping vegetables, dusting perhaps. She might enjoy looking at photographs of Jedburgh or listening to the sorts of songs she might have sung with her school children. Carers might need to listen for the way things connect in her talking, taking careful note of names of people and places so that they can respond to her. This might take time.

Jane Arnell's talk is even more difficult to follow as she is beginning to lose control over the words she wants to use, so she calls the place she's in a 'mental home'. Seeing her words written down makes the meanings come out more clearly. Perhaps you've noticed that we began this unit with her words. She's clearly someone who has a strong sense of other people's needs, as well as her own. She may be someone who is sociable but who needs to be reassured about her own identity, living as she does in a crowded setting.

We've been focusing on the past, on memory, but one thing you might have felt while you read through John Killick's chapter is just how much these older people are talking about the present, even the future. Talk about past identities is important if carers are to be able to focus on the individual and not only on the illness. In remembering, as we've seen, we use the past to make sense of who we are today and to convey that to others. Fragmented and incomplete memories still play that role as do the emotions with which they are conveyed. The accounts of Albert Edwards, Jessie Jamieson and Jane Arnell present opportunities for establishing continuities in people's lives and thus a more complete sense of who they are and want to be.

Care planning, as we saw in Block 2, depends on getting to know someone, and when the context or location in which they are known changes, or if their ability to communicate is diminished, then a life history approach may be an appropriate way to initiate contact and care. Killick's work draws attention to the need to listen and give time to people who are not able to give a coherent or conventional account of themselves. As a writer he tends to focus on a written text which he can then share with the people he works with. Some people with a dementing illness may not have much speech at all. Care workers may well develop their own ways of communicating in such circumstances, for example, by presenting a biography or identity to someone through photographs, taped music or objects. In some way, recognition may be stimulated and identity communicated through movements, gestures or sounds.

Earlier in the course in Unit 7 you looked at Goffman's work on life in institutions. He was an observer, noting down details of the behaviour of staff and inmates in the various places he was researching. What he came up with was fairly depressing as far as institutional life is concerned. It's interesting to see, from Killick's work as well as others, how encouraging people to talk about themselves, their past lives, also brings out information and their feelings about the present. What these accounts do is fill out the gaps in Goffman's analysis, providing us with insights into the lives of people for whom illness and a change of context has threatened the communication of their identity. Through Killick's work as a writer we read their words and almost hear their voices as they are prompted and drawn to talk about themselves and the people and things important to them in their present lives. His approach, and that of others who have developed similar techniques, is helpful to workers and carers as well as, of course, to those for whom residential care is appropriate, and provides a counter to those practices which Goffman identified as typical of institutional living, batch treatment and the denial of individual choice and routine.

> **Key points**
>
> - People with dementing illnesses continue to communicate their identities right through their illness.
>
> - Listening and responding to what they have to say about themselves is a helpful means of preserving their sense of who they are.
>
> - By listening to individual accounts we can help to avoid stereotyping people in terms of their illness.
>
> - When people talk about the past they will also be telling us how they feel about the present and the future.

Conclusion

At the beginning of this unit we set out four core questions. Let's look at them again and see how far we have been able to find answers.

- Why is a sense of identity so important?
- What factors threaten a sense of identity?
- How can identity be maintained and supported in adverse circumstances?
- How best can people be supported in communicating their identity?

We have seen how changes in people's circumstances, the onset of illness, loss of family members, relocation, traumatic experiences, can threaten or undermine people's ability to sustain or communicate their identity, a sense of who they are. We've also seen how change and loss may tend to affect the ways in which other people see them – they may become stereotyped or labelled in terms of their illness or the context in which they live.

We've seen how talking and listening to people about their past experience can be helpful at all life stages and how some theories of identity development, for example Erikson's, can provide a framework within which to locate the issues which confront people at different points in their lives.

We've seen how memory and the past are central to understanding and communicating identity and we've looked at different ways in which work with individual accounts of the past can be helpful and supportive.

Working with people from childhood to old age means developing strategies which are appropriate and in which partnerships may emerge. Workers in health and social care may not always find that this is an easy process. Some people may choose not to remember, others may feel they have no choice but to remember and that this may be a painful process. We've looked at various strategies to deal with difficult emotions and we've also heard from people for whom remembering has been a positive and creative process.

We've worked across the age range and we've seen how identity may be threatened at all stages of life. Our focus has been the need to understand the whole person, both now and in the past, as a basis for developing sensitive and individualised care practice.

Study skills: Your student identity

We've been talking about identity in this unit. What about your emerging identity as a student? Has your idea of yourself changed since you started K100? Thinking about yourself as a student, how would you describe yourself? What kind of a student are you?

Try writing a brief description of your strong points and weak points as a student and your overall prospects of success. Better still, do three versions – one as you think fellow students see you, one as you think your tutor sees you and one as you see yourself. When you've done it put it in your diary folder. Then you can come back to it at the end of the course and see whether your sense of your student identity has changed.

References

Andrews, B. (1997) 'Dark episodes and scar tissue on the psyche', *Times Higher Educational Supplement*, 11 April.

Ara, S. and Chatterjee, D. (1995) *Home to Home: Reminiscences of Bangladeshi Women in Sheffield*, Sheffield City Libraries, Sheffield.

Atkinson, D. (1993) '"I got put away": Group based reminiscence with people with learning difficulties' in Bornat, J. (ed.) *Reminiscence Reviewed: Perspectives, Evaluations, Achievements*, Open University Press, Buckingham.

Barnes, P. (1995) 'Growth and change in adolescence' in Barnes, P. (ed.) *Personal, Social and Emotional Development of Children*, The Open University, Milton Keynes, Blackwell, Oxford.

Bousquet, B. and Douglas, C. (1991) *West Indian Women at War: British Racism in World War II*, Lawrence & Wishart, London.

Butler, R. (1963) 'The life review: an interpretation of reminiscence in the aged', *Psychiatry*, Vol. 26, pp. 65–76.

Campbell, J. and Oliver, M. (1996), *Disability Politics: Understanding Our Past, Changing Our Future*, Routledge, London.

Coleman, P. (1993) 'Reminiscence within the study of ageing: The social significance of story' in Bornat, J. (ed.) *Reminiscence Reviewed: Perspectives, Evaluation, Achievements*, Open University Press, Buckingham.

Coleman, J.C. and Hendry, L. (1990, 2nd edn) *The Nature of Adolescence*, Routledge, London.

Davin, A. (1996) *Growing Up Poor: Home, School and Street in London, 1870–1914*, Rivers Oram Press, London.

Erikson, E.H. (1977, originally published 1950) *Childhood and Society*, Triad/Granada, Bungay.

Erikson, E.H. (1968) *Identity: Youth and Crisis*, Faber & Faber, London.

Evers, H. (1981) 'Care or custody? The experiences of women patients in long-stay geriatric wards' in Hutter, B. and Williams, G. (eds) *Controlling Women: The Normal and the Deviant*, Croom Helm, London.

Ferguson, M. (ed.) (1993) *The History of Mary Prince, a West Indian Slave, Related by Herself*, University of Michigan Press, Michigan.

Fuller, G. (ed.) (1993) *Potter on Potter*, Faber & Faber, London.

Gibson, F. (1991) *The Lost Ones: Recovering the Past to Help their Present*, Dementia Services Development Centre, University of Stirling.

Gibson, F. (1994) 'What can reminiscence contribute to people with dementia?' in Bornat, J. (ed.) *Reminiscence Reviewed: Perspectives, Evaluations, Achievements*, Open University Press, Buckingham.

Giddens, A. (1991) *Modernity and Self-Identity*, Polity Press Ltd, Cambridge.

Goffman, E. (1961) *Asylums*, Penguin Books, London.

Kitwood, T. (1997) 'The uniqueness of persons in dementia' in Marshall, M. (ed.) *State of the Art in Dementia Care*, Centre for Policy on Ageing, London.

McGuire, A. (1997) *False Memory Syndrome: A Statement*, British Association for Counselling, Rugby.

Malone, C., Farthing, L. and Marce, L. (eds) (1996) *The Memory Bird*, Virago.

Middleton, D. and Edwards, D. (1990) 'Conversational remembering: a social psychological approach' in Middleton, D. and Edwards, D. (eds) *Collective Remembering*, Sage, London.

Mihill, C. (1995) 'Celebrations "reviving war trauma in veterans"', *Guardian*, 27 April, p. 6.

Murray, R.N. (1996) *Lest We Forget: The Experiences of World War II West Indian Ex-service Personnel*, Hansib Publishing, Nottingham.

Parker, T. (1997) *Studs Terkel: A Life in Words*, HarperCollins, London.

Persaud, R. (1993) 'Talking your way out of trouble', *Sunday Times*, 26 September.

Pietrukowicz, M.E. and Johnson, M.M.E. (1991) 'Using life histories to individualize nursing home staff attitudes towards residents', *The Gerontologist*, Vol. 31, No. 1, pp. 102–6.

Plaza, D. (1996) 'Family structure and social change of Caribbeans in Britain: an exploratory study of elderly Caribbean males', paper prepared for the Caribbean Studies Association XXI Annual Conference, Puerto Rico.

Rocher, G. (1972) *Talcott Parsons and American Sociology*, Nelson, London.

Ryan, T. and Walker, R. (1993) *Life Story Work*, British Agencies for Adoption and Fostering, London.

Stacey, M. (1988) *The Sociology of Health and Healing: A Textbook*, Routledge, London.

Taylor, R. and Ward, A. (1995) *The Day of the Hillsborough Disaster: A Narrative Account*, Liverpool University Press, Liverpool.

Thompson, P. (1988) *The Voice of the Past: Oral History*, Oxford University Press, Oxford.

Van der Vliet, V. (1996) *The Politics of AIDS*, Bowerdean, London.

Widgery, D. (1991) *Some Lives! A GP's East End*, Simon & Schuster, London.

Acknowledgements

Grateful acknowledgement is made to the following sources for permission to reproduce material in this unit:

Text

Ryan, T. and Walker, R. (1993) *Life Story Work*, British Agencies for Adoption and Fostering; Price, N. (1997) 'My job', *Woman*, 2 June 1997, © Natasha Price; From *Active Life*, July/August 1996, by permission of Aspen Specialist Media; 'The other Lib group on the march', *London Evening Standard*, 28 August 1971; Mullin, J. (1994) '"Forgotten" veterans raise glasses of rum punch', *The Guardian*, 28 April 1994, © Guardian Newspapers Ltd; Advert from *The Guardian*, 30 April 1997, courtesy of Jewish Care; Raman Mundair (1996) 'Poem – Childhood', in Malone, C., Farthing, L. and Marce, L. (eds) *The Memory Bird, Survivors of Sexual Abuse*, Virago, a division of Little, Brown and Company (UK).

Illustrations

p.10 (bottom left): David Gee / *Woman*; *p. 10 (top right)*: this material first appeared in *Professional Social Work*, the magazine of the British Association of Social Workers and reproduced by kind permission; *p. 10 (centre right)*: Courtesy of CAFOD; *p. 11*: Reproduced from Henry Mayhew, *London Labour and the London Poor*, 1861–62; *p. 13*: Sally Greenhill, © Sally and Richard Greenhill; *p. 16 (left)*: © Jamie Knight; *p. 32 (left)*: Gordon Rainsford, courtesy of London Lighthouse; *p. 32 (right)*: Frank Tewkesbury, *London Evening Standard* / SOLO; *p. 36*: Vaughan Melzer; *p. 37*: Copyright Sydney Shelton; *p. 39*: Courtesy: Heritage Recording Unit, Bradford Industrial Museum; *p. 43 (top)*: Trustees of the Imperial War Museum; *p. 43 (bottom)*: Copyright Mark Salmon: *p. 48*: Copyright David Mitchell.

Unit 15
Group Life

Prepared for the course team by Joanna Bornat

While you are working on Unit 15, you will need:
- Course Reader
- Offprints Book
- *The Good Study Guide*
- Block 4 video part 1, 'Better than bingo'
- Media Notes

Contents

Introduction

In Unit 14 our focus was the individual, their life history and the way identities are constructed and presented through talking and remembering. In this unit we look at individual lives in the context of groups.

Group collection

Tap dancing group

Post-natal support group

Groups of choice.

Learning group

Team group

In one way or another most people spend quite a lot of their lives in groups. Sometimes group membership becomes compulsory. Say, for example, you suddenly have to go into hospital and you find that you've become a patient living on a ward. A crisis in the life of a family may mean that children are taken into care, living in a group residential setting, or learning how to become a foster child in someone else's family group. Then there are groups of choice: an OU tutorial group, a football team, a slimming group, a choir, a gym, a holiday tour group.

To say 'choice' is of course to gloss over the fact that although people may choose to join certain groups they can't choose who else joins them! Groups are a bit like families in that respect. In fact you might wonder if the family isn't the basic group that most people start off in. At the other end of the scale you might wonder if the communities described in Unit 11 aren't also examples of another kind of group.

Some groups link their members to help and support, for example a day centre, a drug or alcohol abuse centre, leaving care groups for young people, a stroke group, or carers' support group. On the other hand there are people who may have been pressed into becoming a member of a therapeutic or support group 'for their own good'.

In some form or another groups exist throughout society but for the purposes of K100 it is important to know what they can do for people engaged in the provision of health and social care. I've identified some core questions to give a more specific focus to the discussion which follows:

Core questions

- What are groups and why are they important in health and social care?
- How do people interact in group settings?
- What is the relevance of differences among group members?
- Can groups help people to care for themselves and for others?

Section 1
Groups in health and social care

Sociologists and psychologists since the 1920s and 1930s have observed
how people interact with one another under certain conditions. They
looked for ways to distinguish group situations like the rush-hour or
football crowds from clubs, families, work situations, churches, rural
communities and villages. By observing groups as well as collecting
evidence from artificial group settings organised as experiments, 'social
groups' came to be identified as:

- *having members who depend on one another*
- *having their own rules about procedures and shared ideas*
- *being small enough so that everyone knows something about each
  other*
- *having some kind of shared goal.*

(Sprott, 1952, pp. 1–56; Douglas, 1976, pp. 3–9)

Working with groups became popular in the 1970s as workers in health
and social care put into practice theories about how people behave in
'social groups'. Douglas, a leading proponent, argued:

> *Group work practice is based on a concept of man [sic] as a constantly
> developing human being in necessary and significant interactions with
> other men. He is shaped by others and is shaping others. He presents an
> inseparable unit of physical, mental and emotional facets, again in
> interaction with others. Development does not cease with childhood, but
> continues through the life cycle. The basic needs beyond the biological
> ones are the needs to belong, to be an important individual, and to
> participate. In the life cycle these needs must be fulfilled in a variety of
> changing small group associations.*

(Douglas, 1976, p. 27)

The work of people such as Douglas was based on assumptions that
group membership could therefore be helpful, or therapeutic,
particularly with a skilled leader. They argued that people are often
members of groups such as their families or neighbourhood and that if
they needed support then these group contacts and relationships also
needed to be part of the picture. They suggested that people can learn
and acquire new skills through group membership, particularly when
they draw on each other's experience, and that sometimes group
membership can help people to understand themselves, a process of
personal development (Milson, 1973, pp. 4–60).

Following up these ideas led many community workers and social
workers in the 1970s and 1980s into identifying people who might be
seen as disadvantaged in some way and whom it was thought might be
helped by taking part in organised group activity. Groupwork in
community and residential settings came to be adopted as a means to
developing more positive self-images, tackling immediate problems and
generally enabling people to speak out and identify their individual and
collective needs.

Community worker (left) working her patch

Groupwork skills were part of social work training from the early 1960s but more recently, in the 1990s, the emphasis on individuals as consumers with individually tailored packages of care, the targeting of services and lack of time for hard pressed staff has meant that working with people in groups has tended to become less prominent in the repertoire of social work skills. There were good reasons for the focus on the individual in the 1990 NHS and Community Care Act. Basic health and social care principles emphasise the importance of individualising people so that they don't disappear under the weight of bureaucratic procedures, stereotypes, generalised rules and formal reporting structures. The changes which the Act brought in were in part a response to service users' complaints that their individual needs had tended to be neglected in the past. In Unit 3 we looked at the move from 'service led' to 'needs led' forms of provision which is part of the spirit of the 1990 Act. In Unit 11 we also saw some examples of how a community-based approach continues though with more focused targets these days. The examples we saw included health promotion and health care work at a Community Health House and with members of the travelling community.

In developing a repertoire of skills for practitioners, Payne, who has worked and taught in the area of social work and social care, argues for a focus on individualisation as a basis for developing respect, commitment to self-determination and being prepared to cope with what may be exceptional or unusual in someone's circumstances (Payne, 1991, pp. 23–5). However, many workers still see the need to develop and foster groupwork skills as a basis for good practice with service users. They argue that the perspectives which Payne identifies can be enhanced through group experiences. And, of course, despite the focus on individualisation, for most people health and social care often happens in groups.

Let's begin by looking back through the course for some examples.

Activity 1 Remembering group life

Allow about 5 minutes Think back through the course. How many examples of group experiences can you identify from among the case studies we've discussed? If you want, add some more of your own, drawing on your own experience of health and social care.

Comment In Unit 1 the focus on the family presents perhaps the most familiar and basic experience of group living. In Unit 2 there are examples of people living on a hospital ward and staff working together in a group. In Unit 3 there's mention of the movement by disabled people working together to change attitudes and remove barriers. In Block 2 the Brights' group experiences include the day unit and a carers' support group as well as family and neighbourhood ties. Then there are the residents at Liberty of Earley House who live in their own homes but within a communal setting. Block 3 is very much about groups with its focus on communities and ways of developing supportive strategies among groups of people. Jim and Marianne in Unit 10 have their own group memberships among the drug users on the streets and the staff working in the day units they've attended. As we've already noted, in Unit 11 we saw two examples of projects based on communities where people were working together to identify health needs. And in Unit 12 there was Dostiyo's work with young Asian women and Moyenda with a membership of black families from the African-Caribbean community. Both these projects depend on group experience to develop support and coping strategies for their members. In this block we've met Jamie Knight who has lived in residential care as part of a group and Paul Theobald who has organised and led groups and is an active member of several others.

As for groups from my own experience, well I can think of becoming a member of a hospital ward as a patient, being on the management committee of a Women's Aid Centre, joining in with the rest of the passengers in a railway compartment to object when someone insisted on shouting down their mobile phone for a lengthy part of the journey ... some of these groups lasted for months, others only a short while.

Some groups are formed through organised settings like residential care, other groups develop or are developed within these settings, and yet others emerge around individuals in the community who are seen as sharing some common characteristic or problem. They all have particular features of their own and yet there are also some similarities in the way they work.

Section 2
Using groupwork in a residential setting

In this course, as we've just seen, you have met many examples of people experiencing care, whether as carers or care receivers, in group settings, rather than one to one. This is not simply a matter of happening to be among other people when you are giving or receiving care as, say, with the people who happen to be around you on a train journey. Where care takes place in a group setting, the group is generally a significant part of the experience, whether for good or ill. Indeed the way the group works can make a major contribution to the effectiveness of the care provided. Being a member of a group exerts powerful influences. When groups function poorly they can be inhibiting and stressful, but skilfully structured and supported, they can be used towards a wide range of ends. Consequently, an understanding of how groups work is a valuable asset for any care giver or user of services.

2.1 A routine house meeting that became a supportive group

Group influences are, not surprisingly, particularly strong in residential settings. This poses problems, but also presents important opportunities. You will see how in a vivid account of an experiment in using groupwork to address some of the challenges of running a residential home for adolescent girls.

Activity 2 | **Group meeting to therapeutic group**

Allow about 20 minutes

Turn to Chapter 17 in the Reader. You might want to read through the chapter first before going back to take notes. Write down:

(a) a list of the aims of the group meetings

(b) whether you think each of the aims was met. Make a note of the evidence in each case.

Comment | (a) These are the aims as I listed them:
- encouraging the verbalising of conflicts
- airing difficulties with staff
- challenging unrealistic (or inappropriate) behaviour
- making sense of the past and thinking beyond the present
- achieving for the young women a sense of ownership and participation in the meetings and of safety and security.

(b) I thought that all these aims were met. This is the evidence I picked out:
- The conversation on page 148 shows how a conflict between those preparing meals and those eating them was verbalised, brought into the open. This led to a proposal to produce menus.
- It seems that relations with staff were discussed very regularly indeed. For example, there was the discussion on page 149

which led to the experiment of staff reducing their involvement in the daily life of the hostel.

- On page 151 we see that 'confronting inappropriate or unrealistic behaviour was accomplished frequently by the group itself ... [though] There were inevitably occasions where it fell to a staff member ...' The use of excessive bad language in the meetings is an example where the young women themselves did the challenging. Another issue which seems to have been discussed frequently is heavy drinking and drug abuse and the ensuing violence.

- When it comes to making sense of the past and future, we see on page 149 that a recurrent theme was trying to make sense of why they were actually living there at all and we are given an extract from one of these discussions. Then, on the next page, we see reference to quiet personal discussions of sexuality, marriage and pregnancy.

- As to ownership of the meetings and participation, the young women took over the chairing of the meetings and after six months were concerned not to miss two hours where anything might happen. When one was ejected she stood outside listening and continuing to comment. The need to be there was strong.

What does the chapter by Duffy and McCarthy tell us about groups?

Even the brief mention of regular house meetings at the start of the chapter tells us about some necessary processes which enable a group of people to live together. There has to be some system for organising what happens when, and for allocating duties to people. And then, because there is a system, there have to be rules of some kind to keep it working, and some form of discipline to back up the rules. There also needs to be ways of sharing information between people, so that everyone is operating within the same general framework. And ideally there should be opportunities for reviewing recent events so that problems can be identified and addressed.

The article also gives support to the idea, put forward in a number of theories of groupwork, that a group formed to serve purposes such as exploration, learning and personal growth will tend to develop through a predictable sequence of stages. Although the accounts use different terms, the general sequence which emerges is:

1   *An initial phase when there is uncertainty in the group and people stay on their guard:* Forming.

2   *A stage when members begin to recognise that power is an issue within the group and start to challenge leaders and each other:* Storming.

3   *A stage where things begin to settle down and patterns, or norms, become established:* Norming.

4   *A highly productive stage when people have come to trust each other and are able to talk about problems and give and receive advice:* Performing.

5   *A final stage – if the group has to come to an end – where members are beginning to disengage but also feeling that they will miss the group:* Mourning.

(Tuckman, 1965; Brown, 1979)

Activity 3   *Stages in the group's life*

Allow about 10 minutes

See whether you can find evidence of these stages in the life of the group described in Chapter 17. Note down anything you see that could be relevant to the five headings.

Comment

Although the authors say that the pattern fitted the broad thrust of theoretical accounts of group development, it isn't absolutely clear how to match up the stages. Here is my attempt.

1   Forming – 'The early meetings centred on allowing the culture to change.'

2   Storming – 'The more staff stood back, the more clients claimed their new-found role and used it to accuse, attack and indicate injustice.'

3   Norming – 'A discussion on bad language led to some restrictions on its overuse in the group.'

4   Performing – 'This was most clearly marked by the commitment people felt to be present. To miss the group meeting was to miss two hours when "anything might happen".' There was also the early realisation that they could change and influence things through the group.

5   Mourning – The group did not need to mourn because it had a continuing life, at least so far as we know from the article.

You might like to pause for just a moment to think back to any group you've been a member of. Do you recognise any of these stages from your experience of group life?

2.2 The role of the group within the hostel

As the group described by Duffy and McCarthy matured, it began to serve useful purposes within the life of the hostel. It enabled new solutions to problems to be found, and helped lower tensions. It encouraged the residents to learn new ways of handling relationships with others. It also helped to reduce the staff/client divide by allowing staff to present themselves in a variety of roles and not simply as authority figures. And it allowed staff better access to what was going on in the hostel at the level of the resident sub-culture: 'The group meeting ... [being] a barometer of the atmosphere ... in the hostel as a whole. ... [T]here was feedback, verbal and non verbal, on all aspects of hostel life'. In other words, the group helped to develop new ideas, attitudes and understandings, and new channels of communication, and it helped to loosen up fixed patterns of hostel life, so that more satisfactory ways of living together could be explored.

2.3 The therapeutic aspect of the group

As well as changing life in the hostel, the group meetings were intended to help the residents themselves to change. Staff did not simply join in the group meetings. They saw the group as a suitable setting in which to encourage these adolescent girls from difficult backgrounds to think about themselves and to explore new ways of behaving. For example, it is clear from the article that outbursts of shouting and violence occurred regularly at the hostel. The idea of verbalising conflicts was to help the girls explore other ways of achieving things than through direct confrontation. The exchange which led to the idea of menus for meals was an early indication to the girls that discussion could resolve issues. Also, following the lines of Glasser's model of reality therapy (mentioned in the article), staff encouraged the girls to explore the consequences of behaviour, and to acknowledge and accept responsibility for their own behaviour. In a supportive, trusting atmosphere they hoped that inappropriate behaviour could be challenged thoughtfully and in an analytical way by the whole group, rather than as a heated clash with an authority figure. For example, where drug taking and excessive drinking are a form of rebellion against authority, a challenge by an authority figure tends to reinforce the pattern, whereas in a group of peers some of these girls began to recognise such behaviour as a problem for themselves. More generally, the opportunity to talk about themselves and be taken seriously was seen as enabling personal growth. These girls were at a stage of development where, as Erikson would see it, identity formation would be a pressing concern. Young people of their age need opportunities to challenge the basis of meaning upon which their lives rest. According to Erikson, peer groups play a central part in this exploration of oneself and one's place in society, but living in a hostel these girls would have difficulty establishing consistent, reliable peer relations. The group meetings provided a regular and controlled setting in which the girls could come together as peers, to talk about themselves and support each other. The authors talk, for example, of a developing sense of privacy and respect for their own affairs.

2.4 Safety and security

The emphasis in this therapeutic side of the group meetings was on exploring personally important issues and rethinking them in the light of other people's ideas. But this could not have happened if group members had felt too threatened and defensive to open up their real concerns, or too hostile to listen to others. So it was seen as essential that the group was run in a way that made group members feel safe and secure. Equally they needed to have a sense of ownership of what went on, a sense that things were not being done to them, but rather they were exploring for themselves. Ownership and a sense of safety are important values in their own right. But here we see that these were more than good intentions – they were absolutely necessary to the purposes of the group meetings.

2.5 Personal growth through group experience

Workers in residential childcare, like Bernadette Duffy and Brian McCarthy, recognise the importance of groups for the young people they work with. Taking part in the group and noticing the stages the group goes through is one part of groupwork, but there's another aspect: personal development and growth. Groups offer opportunities for their members to perform a range of different roles. Someone may emerge as the person who's good at thinking up new ideas. Someone else may be the 'peacemaker', trying to defuse tension. We get a brief insight into how this might have been happening in the hostel group when we read that 'A practice developed whereby a group member would have responsibility for "initiating" a new client both to hostel life in general and to the group in particular.' In this case, roles were allocated by the group and also, it seems, judged. As the group matures it's likely that members will develop particular roles, possibly starting the talking, making sure that 'rules' are kept, being the person who calms people down, or perhaps suggesting what to discuss next time. They might also come to recognise the person who becomes the 'scapegoat' for the group, or who tends to be the bully, or a non-stop talker. In this way particular strengths and positive contributions are reinforced as well as less acceptable characteristics, new roles tried out and recognised by group members and by the individuals themselves. Group meetings can thus be used to provide opportunities for personal growth and for learning new responses to social situations.

Study skills: Sharing 'ownership' of 'tutorials'

Many of the same points can be made about the way tutorials work in this course. They are not occasions for you to be told things. Rather they are opportunities for you to explore your own responses to the course, to make better sense of the new ideas you are forming, to reflect on your experiences as a student, and to clarify the meaning and purpose of your studies. Perhaps most important of all, tutorials bring the opportunity of sharing experiences with other people and of developing new insights, drawn from their experience. A sense of ownership and safety is important. It is easy to slip into the role of an observer on the sidelines, watching the expert tutor and the more confident students do their thing. But the tutorial can only work properly for you if you have a sense of being a full participant in what is going on. Scan quickly back through Section 2 of Chapter 3 in *The Good Study Guide* and think about your own involvement in study groups.

We have seen, then, that groups are much more than just a bunch of people in one place. A group has a life of its own. Certain basic structures need to be in place for it to function. But once started, it develops its own momentum and its own agendas. The processes that go on within groups can have powerful effects upon us. Because of this, work with groups needs to establish rules and boundaries which provide a sense of safety and ownership. They need to ensure that individual voices are heard. Yet at the same time group processes require skilful management and support.

In the rest of this unit I will go on to look at some of these aspects in more detail.

Key points

- When people live in a group setting certain fundamental issues arise regarding organisation, rules, discipline, exchange of information and reviewing of events.

- Groups tend to develop through a series of stages. People have to get to know each other and resolve issues of power before they can develop sufficient trust to work on significant problems.

- An open exploratory series of group meetings can have an effect on relationships throughout an organisation.

- Group meetings can be used to provide opportunities for personal growth and for learning new responses to social situations.

- But for this kind of personal development it is essential to have an atmosphere of security and a sense of shared ownership of the group process.

Section 3
Development through group activity

When people get together in groups it's usually for a purpose. Sometimes the setting will determine what kind of group is formed and what its purpose is. We've just looked at the way a group set up for one purpose, a routine house meeting in a hostel for adolescent girls, grew into another kind of group with quite different outcomes for everyone concerned. In some settings it may be necessary to find a way to foster or support group activity, perhaps to 'invent' a group experience for people. Working with older people in day centres, residential care and in some hospital settings, carers have turned to what has come to be known as 'reminiscence work' as a focus for group activity. Already in Unit 14 we saw how this might work on a one-to-one basis, particularly with people who have a dementing illness. We're going on to look at how this approach to supporting a group of older people in a day and residential care setting led to individual and shared outcomes for those who took part.

3.1 An example from Margate

Millmead Linked Service Centre in Margate is run by Kent Social Services. It aims to serve the local community, providing personal care at home, short stay and respite care and longer stay residential care for older people. The centre provides 20 day care places, 20 short stay and respite care places, three emergency beds and 20 longer term residential beds for physically or mentally frail older people. Like other seaside areas, Margate and district has seen many people choose to move in as they retire. Millmead Linked Service Centre aims to meet the needs of these and local older people.

Millmead's operations are determined by the Thanet Elderly Service Provision Group whose aims are threefold:

- *value for money, quality care service to our customers*
- *flexible services in response to each individual's needs as they are assessed*
- *to be a focal point for the community, offering support, guidance and advice.*

(*Kent County Council Social Services Department, 1995*)

In seeking to achieve these aims the centre provides a number of services. These include:

Crisis response, domiciliary care, meals service and delivery, reminiscence loan service, bathing, carer support, hairdressing, chiropody, room hire, work placements.

Reading through the list you might have wondered what is meant by 'reminiscence loan service' and how this can help in achieving the aims which Millmead has had set out for it. Part 1 of the video will give you some answers.

Activity 4   **Remembering at Millmead**

Allow about 45 minutes

This activity is based on the first of the two video programmes: 'Better than bingo: working with reminiscence' on the video cassette for Block 4. This programme shows you how older people who use Millmead Linked Service Centre are encouraged to reminisce and talk about their past lives.

You can find out more about Millmead and the making of the video in the Media Notes. Either read them now before you watch the video or wait till later once you know what 'Better than bingo' is about.

Watch the programme through once. It's about 18 minutes long. Then watch it again, using the pause and rewind buttons if you need to. As you watch a second time think about and make notes on:

(a)   what you think people were saying about 'doing reminiscence'

(b)   how you feel reminiscence contributes to the aims of Millmead as part of Thanet Elderly Service Provision Group.

Comment   What did people say about reminiscence? I noted down a number of things different people said:

Rita Weightmore says 'It brought back memories I thought were completely non-existent'.

Annie Scriven mentioned 'getting to know other people's stories and their type of life'.

Gary Baker talks about seeing 'someone creating something in their later life ... it's a positive, and they're talking about, and they're laughing' ... it's got to be better than playing bingo ... it's got to be'.

Mark Blake who is the unit manager suggests that reminiscence for some people might be 'their first encounter with a large group of people for a long time'.

Mel Channing, a care worker, says 'It's a good way of actually getting to know a resident' and she also points out that 'they feel, I think, they're actually putting something back into society by telling you things that you obviously don't know yourself'.

Later Gary also mentions that reminiscence can be 'trauma' or 'upsetting'.

Rita Weightmore says 'If it's a fact, if it's happened in the past, it's happened, and I don't think it's bad at all to reminisce and remember – makes you appreciate how good it is living today'.

And what did you note down about the way reminiscence contributes to the aims of the centre?

It seems as if the reminiscence work we saw in the video matches all those aims. Jane O'Leary, the services manager, points out how cost effective the work is, Mark Blake stresses the contribution which reminiscence makes to knowing the whole person, which is important when responding to individual needs, and Gary points out how work for the life story books provides 'background information which you wouldn't get from a normal form'. Both he and Jane O'Leary also emphasise the links which the reminiscence loans service makes with other local agencies. The reminiscence boxes are lent out and sometimes form the basis for work with local schools and museums. There is also mention of the importance of seeing people as individuals and understanding how someone's 'past history can affect how they are now'.

You'll remember that in Unit 14 we saw how remembering the past can be helpful at different stages in people's lives and how a biographical approach to care and support can lead to individualised outcomes and perhaps a more sensitive approach on the part of carers. The video showed all these principles at work but, as we've seen and heard, the group setting brought 'added value' for the group members and the staff who work with them. In the next two sections we're going to look in more detail at the way group life develops through talk and discussion with a view to identifying how individuals work in groups.

CLIENT INFORMATION

ADMISSION DETAILS:

Emergency	Assessment	Short Term	Phased Care	Permanent	Domiciliary	Day Care
☐	☐	☐	☐	☐	☐	☐

Key Worker : _____

Genysis Number: _____

Admission Date: / /

Discharge Date: / /
Permanent Date: / /

SURNAME:	**CARE MANAGER:**	**PERSONAL DESCRIPTION:**
FORENAME(S):	Tel:	Height:
a.k.a.	Base:	Colour of Hair:
D.o.B:　　　**Marital Status:**	Risk Assessment?　Yes/No	Complexion:
Home Address:	Date:	Build:
	DOCTOR:	Weight:
	Practice Name:	Sight:
Town:	Tel:	Hearing:
County:　　　Post Code:	Address:	Speech:
Tel:		**GENERAL INFORMATION**
Ethnic Origin:		
First Language:	**MEDICAL INFORMATION/KNOWN**	
Religion:	**ALLERGIES:**	
NEXT OF KIN:		
Relationship:		
Contact Telephone Numbers:		
Day:　　　**Eve:**		
Address:		
Town:		
County:　　　Post Code:		
MAIN CONTACT:		
Relationship:		
Contact Telephone Numbers:		
Day:　　　**Eve:**		

Record keeping at Millmead: keeping a record of the basic information on each individual

Study skills: Studying with video cassettes

You have used the skills video for exploring caring skills. Now in this block you are using video in a way that is more similar to your previous work with audio cassettes. Do you find it a good medium to learn from? What do you think video teaches well? Does it have any disadvantages from a study point of view? How much of your precious study time does it deserve? Will you view it several times? Does video require special study skills?

Try jotting down some answers to these questions based on your experience so far? Then read Sections 4 and 5.1 of Chapter 3 of *The Good Study Guide* (pp. 72–80) and see whether you came to similar conclusions.

3.2 Group structures and group life

There are several things to look out for in groups. There's the role of the leader or facilitator. Then there's the formal as well as the informal life of the group and also the possibilities and limitations of group life. Let's think back to the reminiscence group at Millmead again. Here we saw a group of six older people with a group leader talking about schooldays. Gary sees his role as group facilitator or leader. He asks the questions. He focuses attention on particular people. He decides when to move on to someone else's story.

In formal terms, so far as Millmead's managers and workers and the older people are concerned, this is a group set up with certain objectives, to talk, listen and generally share memories. Sociologists help us to understand groups when they distinguish *formal* and *informal* activities. By *formal* they mean that the group can be seen as having recognised characteristics and rules of membership which all who take part are aware of. The formal rules of the Millmead group seem to be that people arrive at the group at a certain time, or they're brought there and they expect to be talking about some aspect of the past that they can all relate to. But there's more to the formal rules than this. To take part people have to be prepared to get to know each other, be prepared to join in and, at times, take their cue from Gary when he asks questions or produces prompts such as the spinning top or the packet of violet scented sweets. They could get up and leave, or ask to go, or they could simply sit and choose to watch rather than join in. The group is organised in such a way that any of these actions could be accommodated without disruption to the group itself. The expectation is, however, that people will join in, and, so far as possible, enjoy themselves at the same time.

Watching the video you probably noticed some moments when things worked for the group and other times when things didn't quite work out. People don't find it easy to take turns when they're talking about what they remember so it was quite noisy and some prompts or questions simply didn't provoke a response at all.

There's much to go on from 'Better than bingo' as far as evidence about the *informal* life of the reminiscence group is concerned. When sociologists talk about the informal life of a group they mean those aspects which may be unplanned or which may develop during the lifetime of the group as people interact with one another. One of the

Gary Baker, Care Worker at Millmead Linked Service Centre

aims of the group is to build understanding and support between members. Gary mentions an occasion when a woman who was distressed by her memories was helped by group members. He felt reassured when this happened since it was evidence for him that group members were building their own understanding and accepting support from each other without his intervention. So far as the group on film is concerned we can see examples of people leaning towards each other, passing round objects and listening. Perhaps one example of informal group ties comes in moments when group members talk about themselves as a group, saying 'We were never allowed sweets at school in those days' or emphatically telling Gary that he's got the wrong kind of spinning top in his memory box. In the short space of time we have to observe the group's life it's possible to see shared and informal understandings emerge.

Activity 5 Formal and informal

Allow about 5 minutes Pause for a moment and look back through the last section about the formal and informal life of the Millmead group and, remembering what you saw on the video, weigh each up. How would you rate the relative importance of formal and informal group life to the people taking part?

Comment Formally, the group exists to get people together in one place and to retrieve memories of the past together, to promote social contact and to enable the staff to develop some sense of the 'whole person' being cared for at Millmead. But you might have felt that the informal life of the group was perhaps more important as you saw how people's individual strengths and abilities to contribute to the group emerged, how their sense of collective and shared experiences was drawn on, how they interacted with one another and seemed to demonstrate their pride and pleasure in their own and each other's experiences and how, from what Gary says, members may even take control of the group as they deal with difficult emotions.

In the next section we go on to look at how talking together, in this case by focusing on past experience, helps both formal and informal aspects of group life to develop.

3.3 Talking in groups

Kevin Buchanan and David Middleton have studied how people talk in reminiscence groups. They suggest that talking about the past enables older people to establish their identities as members of particular communities and in relation to other individuals at that time. It is a way of establishing what they call 'membership in the past' (Buchanan and Middleton, 1995). There's an example of this in the Millmead group when Mel Fisher talks about getting her first job:

Mel Fisher, member of the Millmead Reminiscence Group

> *Well, you were supposed to leave at 14 but as my father lost his job just before then, I had to stay on at school because he wouldn't get any dole for me, and then when you were 15 you had to leave so I had to go to what they called an instruction centre, but we called it the dole school. We had to go there before he got any money for us. Well, I'd been there a few weeks and I got a job as a tailoress, and I was lucky because then you had to pay if you were an apprentice, but I got paid, so I was a tailoress until the war started and I went into the army.*

Did you notice the way Mel Fisher spoke? She moves from 'I' to 'we' in her account. She is establishing herself as that person in the past and telling the story of what happened when she was old enough to leave school: 'I had to stay on at school ...'. At the same time she is locating herself in that past, as a member of a generation at that time to whom certain things happened and who had their own perspective, even language: 'we called it the dole school'. We learn something from Mel Fisher – she can tell us about the past, in this case about unemployment in the north east of England. This is oral history, evidence about the past from people who lived in it and who have memories of past times. At the same time, in remembering or reminiscing, she is telling her audience about what kind of a person she was then. This also helps her and the group she is a part of to place her in terms of her past and current identities.

When people talk about the past together, Buchanan and Middleton argue, they are also locating themselves in the present as members of a group which exists today. If you think back to the video you'll remember that while Mel Fisher was speaking, other members of the group were joining in, agreeing with her. In this way remembering becomes a way of establishing a group or generational experience. We can see how this works from the sequence where the sweets are shared out:

> Gary: *And how about like for instance, we were saying about sweets, was you allowed sweets at school?*
>
> *Everyone says no.*
>
> Gary: *No?*
>
> *Everyone says not.*
>
> Gary: *Right now I'm going to offer some of these round because we're ...*
>
> Annie: *They were taken away from us and put in the wastepaper basket.*
>
> Gary: *Were they really?*
>
> Annie: *Yes, I was never allowed sweets in school.*
>
> Gary: *You wasn't allowed sweets in school? Does anybody know what these are?*
>
> Rita: *Yes, they're violet scented ... Parma Violets.*
>
> Gary: *That's right. Do you want to pass them round Mel? Do you remember those?*
>
> Rita: *I remember those and sweet lips, do you remember the pink sweet lips?*
>
> Gary: *Er, no, no.*
>
> Rita: *I remember I thought it was lovely if you had some of those in your pocket.*

In talking about their memories of sweets Annie Scriven, Rita Weightmore and the other members of the group are invoking a common set of experiences, one which is rooted in their particular generation's own history. It is a shared experience as we have already seen but in terms of the reminiscence group it is also a way of building links between them. Thus they come to have a common identity not only as the children they were once were, but as the older people they are now. This even extends to Rita asking Gary if he remembers those same sweets and almost anticipating his negative answer because she and the group are establishing that they are part of a different social group defined in terms of age.

3.4 Making use of group talk

Formally the reminiscence group exists as a means for organising discussion around certain topics, and as Gary explains, this can provide him and his co-workers with more information about the people they are working with. This has positive consequences for the quality of care they feel they are able to deliver. If someone shows signs that they are feeling sad or for some reason isn't able to participate fully, this also interests Gary. He makes sure that his colleagues are aware of any changes or particular reactions which individual members of the group have.

Informally the group clearly has its own life, with members managing and directing the discussion at times. By listening closely not only to what people say, but how they say it and to whom, it becomes clear that talking about the past is not just a question of remembering.

Faith Gibson's evaluation of reminiscence groups in residential and day care settings in Northern Ireland reveals changes for people in 25 reminiscence groups observed. She points out that, in the case of people living in residential care:

> ... *many had lived in close proximity to each other for years ... [but] ... sharing the same residential home had not meant shared lives. Through reminiscing in groups they discovered common origins and past experience of which they had no inkling. For such people living private lives in public places it was as if group reminiscence served the dual purpose of putting them in touch with their personal past as well as putting them in touch with other people in the present. In this way the then and there enriched the here and now.*

Perhaps almost as important, staff attitudes changed:

> *In my first meeting with the head of unit I had been told about a Mr G who would not be included because he would be unlikely to talk due to a recent stroke and serious depression. In a second meeting I was again told he was too depressed and difficult to work with ... At the first group meeting he was wheeled in and I was again warned not to expect too much. For the first 10 minutes Mr G just stared at the screen. If we asked him a question he just shook his head. Then we showed the slide of the poteen still. He smiled and told us two stories about poteen makers he knew who were nearly caught.*
>
> *He became one of the major contributors on nearly every slide ... His face glowed. His eyes shone and he ended the session by saying he had not enjoyed himself so much for a long time. He then went off to lunch and kept talking about the old days. He continued to attend and actively participate in all the sessions.*
>
> *(Gibson, 1992, pp. 34–35)*

What Gibson and other observers have noted is the way participating in group remembering can help to bring out individual attributes, hidden abilities, sometimes hidden histories. As far as Gary Baker and his colleagues at Millmead are concerned, these individual accounts form an essential part of care delivery. But what about work with other groups? Can the way stories and personal experience emerge have the same function?

In Unit 14, Section 1 there was a brief example from a group of older people with learning disability illustrating the way in which membership in a group can have particular significance and how collective remembering can have a range of unexpected outcomes (Atkinson, 1994). These were people who had spent much of their lives in institutional care but who latterly had moved into residential and day care settings. After Atkinson had worked with the group for some time she looked back through what they'd been saying and saw that there was more going on than simply talk about the past.

She describes this group as moving through four phases:

Phase 1: 'Public' accounts – she introduced topics all the group could identify with and which were not threatening.

Phase 2: Period details – she produced various prompts, audio tapes, photographs, cigarette cards – items typical of the group members' younger days.

Phase 3: 'Private' accounts – working in smaller groups of two and three, people came out with more personal memories – they were able to talk about painful events and reflect on them.

Phase 4: A collective account – the transcripts of the meetings were edited into drafts of a book and each reading brought out more memories leading to further drafting.

These phases overlapped often and she stresses that although they represent a trend in the direction of the group's life, certain phases also occurred more than once. The final phase was characterised by the emergence of collective memories as people began to share accounts of living in different hospitals. From this a sort of consensus about hospital life emerged, one which Atkinson suggests 'served to sustain and justify the group's distinctive history, a history which hitherto has largely remained hidden or marginalized' (1994, p. 101).

Ryan and Walker describe very similar outcomes from the group life history work they've done with children who are in care or fostered. They say:

> *Children who are looked after often consider that their families are abnormal and it can be a revelation to them that their families are like many others. One group of five children discovered in their exploration that not only had none of them ever met their fathers, or had not done so for many years, but also that they all came from many-fathered families and all had half-brothers and sisters. No amount of assurance from an adult could, we feel, have helped these children to place their families in context as 'normal' as much as talking and sharing with their peers had.*
>
> *(Ryan and Walker, 1993, p. 49)*

From Ryan and Walker, 1993, p. 51

Key points

- Groups may be set up and run for more than one purpose.

- Groups have formal structures and rules of management which members will usually be aware of and which give the group its name, description and agreed objectives.

- Groups also have informal structures which may develop during the life of the group among members.

- Talk in groups is not just a matter of telling a story or recounting experience, it's a way of establishing individual and group identities.

- Collective remembering can be helpful to individuals who may feel isolated or have negative feelings about their own experiences.

Section 4
Groups and diversity

So far we have concentrated on groups of people in care settings to focus on how groups work. We've looked in detail at the ways in which talk about the past can help to form group bonds and confirm people as individuals and as part of, in this case, a generational or particular type of experience. We saw how some people gain from being in groups with people who have had similar experiences to their own, but is that always the case, or even always possible to arrange?

4.1 Differences within groups

All the groups we've looked at so far have shown evidence of strong cohesion; even if their members fall out from time to time, they share enough common characteristics to be able to maintain their membership and carry on. What we haven't looked at yet are groups which may work well for *some* people, but which may not meet the needs of, or actually exclude, *other* people.

Activity 6 | **Being aware of difference**

Allow about 5 minutes | Think back to the Millmead and hostel groups described earlier in this unit. We talked about them as if they were made up from particular types of people: frail older people, adolescent young women. We focused on what brought them together, but what about some of the differences among their members? Jot down a few that you noticed or perhaps imagined. How important are the differences you picked out?

Comment | Among the Millmead group I noticed that there were differences of: gender, disability, age, region, education, class, reasons for being at Millmead.

For the hostel group it wasn't so easy because we don't actually get introduced to them as individual members. But we were told that some had 'lived rough', others had come straight from 'intolerable circumstances at home', while others had 'been referred by social workers'. There might have been marked differences in clothing and hairstyle as well as ethnicity and educational experience. I imagine that there might be some differences in size as well, with some members appearing much more physically powerful than others.

It's difficult to know whether any of these real or imagined differences might be significant without having an opportunity to talk to the group members. Anyway, sometimes people will 'swallow their differences' if they feel it's more important to focus on what brings them together. At Millmead it was physical and mental frailty, in the case of the young women living in the hostel it was a shared experience of rejection, and the need for social and psychological support.

The members of the Millmead group shared a number of characteristics even if, judging from their north east of England accents, Mel Fisher and Rita Weightmore grew up several hundred miles away from Kent. They are all of a like age, they live in the Margate area, they seem to come from similar social backgrounds, but most obviously, they are all white, older, English-born people. How easy might it have been for someone from an Asian, African-Caribbean or Irish background to fit in with this group? Remember the older African-Caribbean man in Unit 14 who said that he 'can't reminisce'? Group facilitators need to make sure that reminiscence groups recognise there will be differences. This can be difficult when awareness of difference has led to oppressive and racist behaviour in the past (Harris and Hopkins, 1994).

Harmonious Reminiscences is an anthology of memories of black pensioners living in the London Borough of Lewisham. The lives they describe include unemployment, marriage, children, work and urban life, but the context of their lives is one in which separation and journeys play a large part. All came to London from the 1950s onwards and although some had returned to the Caribbean several times, others had never been back. Alberta Kirkland remembered difficult times:

> *... I saw two white boys and they said 'You black bastard!' and they threw something in my eyes and I stood up there and I couldn't see because I was blacked out ... things were very bad between the blacks and the whites. That was the time in England when some white people used to spit in the faces of blacks.*
>
> *(Lewisham West Reminiscence Group, 1993, p. 36)*

Memories like these might prove difficult to relate outside a group of black people who had shared similar experiences and developed their own ways of coping with racist and oppressive behaviour. These memories need to be heard and acknowledged; however, they may not be spoken unless people feel confident that they will be given a sympathetic and supportive hearing.

Chapeltown Black Women Writers' Group published their experiences of living in Britain

One problem which group leaders and members may not always be aware of is the way some kind of consensus or conformity is arrived at within the group. Sometimes it's difficult to go against what everyone else is saying, to 'step out of line'. It may feel easier to emphasise how much you share rather than how different you feel. Perhaps that's why in some social situations people will stipulate 'no religion and no politics' when it comes to chat. The problem is that individual viewpoints may not get a hearing if there is too strong a sense of a single group identity. Although it's tempting to look for ways to express solidarity and collective strength, if there's too much then it may actually prevent the group achieving what it set out to do. Some individual members may feel disempowered, unrepresented and therefore isolated within the group.

Conformity may of course be only 'skin deep'. Members of groups may choose to appear to conform, showing compliance, while privately disagreeing strongly. And of course if conformity is strong then it will be that much more difficult for the group to find out that it's actually making a mistake or misjudgment. Later in the course, in Unit 24, we'll be looking at complaining and whistle-blowing and finding out just how difficult it can be to resist group and organisational pressures. At this stage we're simply considering the ways in which the experience of being or feeling different can lead to exclusion from or being marginalised in groups.

Activity 7   Majority or minority?

Allow 2–3 minutes   Pause for a moment and think about two occasions, one when you were in a majority in a group, one when you were in a minority. What did it feel like? Jot down some words that you associate with each experience.

Comment   I don't know what your experiences might have been. It could have been when everyone round you is speaking your own language. It could have been in an argument when nearly everyone agreed with you, or you told a joke and everyone laughed. It could have been suddenly realising that you were the only man at an OU tutorial group, or it could have been noticing that you're the only woman wearing trousers at a public event. Perhaps you've been the 'token' black person at a meeting or the oldest person at a party.

For one of our course testers this activity brought back memories of her OU tutorials: 'When I first started studying with the OU I was by far the oldest in my group, it being 30 years since I had left school. I never really joined in because I felt I could not compete with the 18 to 20-year-old 'whizz-kids'. It took a long time for me to feel that I could contribute anything constructive to the group'.

Someone else remembered being in Nigeria nearly 30 years ago and feeling 'incredibly intimidated' in some parts of the country where she was the only white person.

Writing this activity made me realise that majority experiences feel more positive than minority experiences. Perhaps that's helpful to remember when working with groups of people who are likely to have more differences between them than similarities.

It's likely that people experience groups in different ways and that group memberships do play an important part in everyone's lives. Given this, it is important to make sure that differences are respected and that minority voices are not only heard but given serious consideration. Sometimes the minority message may not be one we want to hear, it may be offensive and repugnant, but by listening to it we may learn something about the person or people who are saying it and how we then deal with what is being said.

4.2 Group membership, same or different?

We've looked at some of the disadvantages of groups which are strongly consensual or which are able to build up a common perspective because their members have similar backgrounds. The problem is that sometimes it may be better if a group is made up from people who share more similarities than differences. How can we judge what's going to work best for everyone? To find an answer to this question I am going to draw on an article by Susan Rice and Catherine Goodman. They describe four different scenarios or 'case examples' of groups. The question they ask is:

> *In composing a group, ... along what variables should people be alike or different? For example, when are age, sex, racial background, religion and social class – the 'demographic variable' – important for matchup, and when does it enhance the group to be mixed on these factors? When are variables such as emotional attitudes, coping mechanisms, specific life crises, and purposes for joining the group best kept as similar as possible, and when should they be mixed in a group?*
>
> (Rice and Goodman, 1992)

Activity 8   Separation or integration?

Allow about 15 minutes   Look at the four scenarios in the box opposite and the arguments for and against groups being made up from members who are more alike than different. Note down what your response would be if you were asked to give your opinion.

Comment   It isn't easy and there is probably no obvious answer as groups all differ from one another. It may be that as a group develops it moves from sameness to difference, or from difference to sameness. An initial shared identity may help to start a group off but it may be more helpful if differences are allowed for later on by dividing the group up into pairs or mini-groups so that people can talk about particular experiences. And of course there's always the issue of budgets restricting the amount of funds available to support more than one group at any time. So far we've been talking about groups among users of services but of course we could also be applying these ideas to groups of workers where issues of single-sex training and harassment may be tackled.

Rice and Goodman suggest that how people choose, either group leaders or members, will depend on broader theories they hold about how groups should work. People who choose difference or heterogeneity tend to see groups as being like the world in miniature with differences providing more opportunities to learn from experience and to feel empowered in their roles.

People who choose likeness or homogeneity tend to emphasise the importance of the group for the feelings of solidarity it can encourage; group cohesion encourages toleration of conflict and the possibility of productive work is increased.

Difference or likeness in groups: some scenarios

1   A group formed for people with learning difficulties who are finding out about moving into the community. Should the group be made up only from new members or would a mix of people who have already settled and people who have yet to make the move be better?

Difference: a mixed group might allow for a range of experience providing people about to move with information and possibly support from the already well established people; a mixed group might help those finding out to feel empowered, particularly if the people who are already established are encouraged to take on a helping role. A mixed group might mean that the new people accomplish the transition into the community with fewer anxieties.

Likeness: people have many different reasons for moving into the community. They may have a long history of institutional care, they may have already had an unsuccessful attempt to move out, they may have varying amounts of contact with their families and friends. It may be that by focusing on the one thing which makes them similar, the move itself, they might find some support. For staff, a group made up entirely of new people means an opportunity to go over the basics and what to expect in careful detail.

2   A group of severely 'clinically depressed' older people at a day centre who are all going through a prolonged grieving process following the death of a spouse. Should the group be made up only of these people, or be a general group including people who are grieving but who are resolving the process with fewer problems?

Difference: because it is difficult to draw a line between 'healthy' and 'unhealthy' grieving it might be difficult to separate out a specific group. People have different ways of coping with grief and what might work for one person might not work for another. A group made up of different people would provide its members with examples of variety in the way people cope with their feelings. In this way the group itself offers a greater variety of resources to its members and people learn from each other the possibility of different strategies in dealing with stages of widowhood.

Likeness: people who are clinically depressed may react in different ways if they meet in a group which has a wide range of intensity of need. They may be unable to help others, they may monopolise the whole group or they may withdraw. A sense of similarity may help people to support one another and if each feels that they are facing similar problems then they may be able to work on these together, listening to each other and arriving at a way of understanding the issue.

3   A group at a day centre for older people looking at issues of ageing which is composed, as it happens, entirely of gay and lesbian members. Should a new member who is heterosexual be introduced who also happens to have an interest in ageing? A similar set of issues might arise if it were suggested that a black person should join a group of white people.

Difference: the argument might be that ageing is a universal experience which cuts across other differences. It might also be the case that by introducing someone from a different background it might be possible to promote integration and greater understanding. Again, difference in perspective may provide people with something to discuss rather than be in conflict over.

Likeness: race, ethnicity and sexual preference all link to particular types of views and understandings of the world and will probably influence who people prefer as friends. Ageing can have very different meanings for someone who is gay or lesbian, as it can for black people, and these will influence the way the topic is discussed. Moreover, one person on their own might well feel excluded if there is a sharing of jokes and references to particular experiences.

4   A support group for carers of people with Alzheimer's disease. Should different carers, the children and the partners of people with the illness, be included in the same group?

Difference: the issues faced by children and partners are basically the same and it's possible that conflicts between generations might better be resolved when these different perspectives are presented by people who are unrelated.

Likeness: there are too many sharply defined differences between these two groups; partners are dealing with issues of sexual intimacy, financial and emotional issues and planning for widowhood; children are dealing with a changed role in relation to a parent and perhaps facing the possibility that there will be some unresolved issues from the parent-child relationship.

(*Adapted from Rice and Goodman, 1992*)

4.3 Organising on the basis of likeness

So far we've been considering likeness and difference as if there is always a clear cut and obvious choice, but sometimes this isn't the case. Sometimes it may be imperative to identify a basis for similarity in order to counteract oppressive and discriminatory behaviour. Disabled people have consistently made a strong case for the need to share common experiences as a basis for changing attitudes, their own as well as those of non-disabled people, building a strong sense of self-worth and pride. Nasa Begum is a black disabled woman who, after years of attending special schools and arguing for the right not to be defined as disabled, says she's changed: '... now I think being disabled is part of my identity'; however, there is still the issue of being seen stereotypically as 'Asian':

> *I guess I just ignored the fact that I was black. It's very easy to do it for black disabled people because other people only concentrate on your disability. It's your disability that gets you sent to Treloars.* [The only grammar school for children with mixed impairments.] *In fact I got put in a lower class because English was my second language. It never occurred to me that this might be racism.*
>
> (*Quoted in Campbell and Oliver, 1996, p. 133*)

Organisations of deaf people have existed since the 1820s and the first schools for deaf people date back to the 1790s. As Paddy Ladd explains: 'Our language is much older ... Our customs and traditions have been passed down through the ages and these, together with our values and beliefs, constitute our culture'. Paddy Ladd's view is that deaf people are a linguistic community first, not simply a disabled group (quoted in Campbell and Oliver, p. 120). Long though the history of this community might be there are still divisions within it, as Kavita Kohli, a deaf social worker, argues (Kohli, 1993, p. 238). Aware of the isolation and racism faced by black deaf people she researched the need for a support group for Asian deaf women in Leicester. Her aims were to:

• encourage members to value and respect themselves

• give members space to develop their abilities and potential in areas that interested them

• encourage members to think about their own needs and explore constructive and creative ways of meeting them

• encourage members to develop and value their friendship network

• provide assistance or support to be self-determining and understand any discrimination or prejudice which members may encounter.

Kohli was the group leader, and as she is an Asian deaf woman herself she felt that she could 'relate immediately to the members'. She was able to communicate in three languages: an Asian language, English and British Sign Language (BSL). She was also aware of Asian cultures and was able to make 'use of my own life experiences construtively to enable others'. She also had a personal and professional understanding of racism.

Some members of the Asian Women's Group at Leicester Centre for Deaf People

The group met three times a month at Leicester Centre for Deaf People and comprised around 10 women between the ages of 18 and 40. In her evaluation of the project she found many advantages in a groupwork approach based on likeness. As Asian deaf women they had not, up until then, found that existing deaf groups had addressed their needs. For people in white deaf groups she argues 'deafness was the only issue', which meant that inequalities and oppression linked to gender and race 'were evaded or ignored' (p. 242). Among the positive achievements she noted were:

- reduced isolation

- enhanced self-confidence and self-esteem – members were 'helped to deal with their negative emotions' by reassuring and supporting one another, being involved in planning group activities

- empowerment – 'identity and cohesion ... highlighted the lack of services for Asian deaf people'

- effective use of social work time and effort – 'as a groupworker with Asian deaf women I came to realise that traditional casework tends to isolate people from the community'.

However, she also noted some problems:

- communication difficulties – many of the members 'had poor standard English and limited BSL skills. They used home-made sign language or personal gestures, and these are not always easy to decipher'

- lack of individual attention – 'there were times when members could not always cope with sharing in a group setting' and there were also issues of confidentiality

- black/ethnic minority deaf people's needs – the importance of tackling racist assumptions and avoiding the danger of groups becoming marginalised

- resources – groupwork needs adequate resourcing (accommodation, transport, equipment, staffing, catering facilities) if it is to be effective.

4.4 Likeness or difference in balance

We've looked at some issues of difference and likeness as these affect groups and groupwork. It seems as if there may be no clearcut answer to questions about shared or diverse characteristics. The examples we've looked at all seem to illustrate that participating in a group can be supportive and enhance a sense of self-worth and belonging. It can also turn people into recognised experts as they come up with accounts about the past, or relate experiences which they have coped with successfully. However the problems of excluding certain people through lack of recognition of particular life events or of their oppression and injustice remains a challenge for all groups. Kavita Kohli felt that she had a better understanding of the members of the Asian Deaf Women's Group in Leicester since she shared what she saw as those characteristics which brought the group together. A solution put forward by Rice and Goodman is to recognise the positive role which difference can play in a group, if difference is recognised and supported. Perhaps an alternative, which Dorothy Atkinson's account suggests, is the need to recognise that there may be both public and private stories and that people need opportunities to tell both, in groups which vary in size or which break up into smaller partnerships.

It may sometimes be the case that workers are not in a position to influence the composition of a group. Sometimes in day and residential settings people make their own groups in lounges, entrance halls and at dining tables. These naturally occurring groups can be worked alongside but their membership is already decided by personal preferences.

Allan Brown and Tara Mistry point out how a lack of sufficient resources may mean that groups mixed by gender or on a cultural basis may be inevitable. There's also the possibility that, as at Millmead, membership is made up of the people who attend a particular centre or unit and to exclude someone when there is no other available alternative might in itself be seen as discriminatory or oppressive. As they also remark, 'many women and black people prefer to be in mixed groups' (Brown and Mistry, 1994, p. 10). It might also be worth noting that although Kavita Kohli shared her deafness and her ethnicity with her group members there were differences. She is a professional, someone with access to educational and training opportunities and consequently has access to a greater range of resources than the women she was working with.

Finally, there's perhaps a need to remember that people are likely to be members of more than one group at any time. Maria Francis-Spence, writing about groupwork with black women, argues the need to redefine groups to include supportive activities which may be quite informal, not practitioner led. She points to hair grooming and shared leisure activities but also suggests that 'groupwork is part of many Black women's culture' (Francis-Spence 1994, p. 113). Talking to and supporting each other through challenges and hurtful experiences is a 'normal part of life for Black women', she argues, but these normal ways of relating need to be accepted as networking and groupwork on their own terms.

Key points

- Though group solidarity and cohesion can be a helpful outcome it's important to recognise that there will be differences among group members.

- Some differences will be difficult to include because they will be experienced as racism and oppression.

- It's important to be able to weigh up the advantages and disadvantages for people of being in same or different membership groups.

- Sometimes it may be an advantage if the leader of a group based on sameness shares some of the same experiences as the group members.

- Group leaders, and members, may need to recognise and accept particular strategies to support individual group experience.

Section 5
Working in groups

In this section we're going back to Millmead for another look at the video 'Better than bingo'. Though we'll be focusing on a particular group of older people and the workers who support them, you'll find it helpful if you try to relate what you see to any group you happen to be familiar with. There are many aspects of groupwork which are not specific to any one group of service users so try to think laterally as you view the video and read through this section.

5.1 Skills in groupwork

Activity 9   **Identifying skills**

Allow about 30 minutes

I want you to watch the whole video again. As before, use the pause and rewind buttons if you need to. Jot down under the names of each person you see what you think they say or do which shows what they contribute to groupwork at Millmead.

Just to remind you, the people you see are:

- Mel Fisher, Edith Houghton, George Mooney, Edith Sampson, Annie Scriven and Rita Weightmore, the older people in the group
- Jane O'Leary, services manager
- Mark Blake, unit manager
- Mel Channing, care worker
- Gary Baker, care co-ordinator and reminiscence worker.

Comment   These are just some things I noticed. You may have come up with others.

The older people: Annie Scriven, Rita Weightmore and the other members of the group are drawing on their lifetime experience of joining in, listening and turn taking when it comes to telling stories or offering their knowledge. Sometimes the turn taking is jettisoned when everyone wants to say what they know, but in the main there are some considerable group participation skills on display here. Not everyone is able to speak at length, so sometimes they intone or make briefer verbal interjections to back up other people. Edith Houghton, for example, says she felt 'terrible' when she left school to find a job as Mel Fisher begins her story and earlier you hear her saying 'Everyone went into service in those days' as Annie begins her story. She's joining in but not necessarily wanting to take the floor.

Jane O'Leary, as services manager, has an overview of the group and how it supports the wider aims of Millmead. She has to be able to back the work that is going on and give it her support. This is not just a question of identifying money in the budget, but giving an account of the work which is understandable to people outside Millmead: her manager, the wider public and other agencies or units which may be competing for resources.

Jane O'Leary, services manager, responsible for Millmead Linked Service Centre

Rita Weightmore

Annie Scriven

George Mooney

Edith Sampson

Edith Houghton

Members of the Millmead Reminiscence Group

Mark Blake, unit manager at Millmead

Mark Blake: as unit manager he also needs to be able to support and provide resources for the reminiscence groupwork. He has control over immediate resources such as staff time, space and daily timetabling. Managers can have a crucial influence on the success or failure of staff enthusiasms such as Gary's. By supporting the work and seeing that its outcomes are part of ongoing care processes at Millmead his role is significant. He enables and encourages staff to join in and through Gary's reporting back on the process he gets a fuller picture of people's lives. As he explains it, 'the whole person' is integrated into the formal pattern of record keeping.

Mel Channing, care worker at Millmead

Mel Channing is a care worker who recognises the contribution which the older people can make not only to the care process, by telling her more about their own lives, but to her own knowledge of the past. She's clear that she learns things from the people she works with at Millmead and that this is a bonus for her. She seems to be good at <u>listening</u>. She points out that not everyone has the same ability to communicate; however she's clear that even those with the greatest needs will have something to say. She <u>values</u> everyone's contributions. She's <u>aware</u> of the effect of disabling conditions and impairment on remembering. She's also aware that what she is told on a one-to-one basis is confidential and should be dealt with appropriately. She's positive about the reminiscence sessions and sees <u>joining in</u> as part of her work.

Gary Baker: I've left Gary till last because he seems to be very much at the centre of things. Gary brings to the group his particular personal attributes, his <u>enthusiasm</u>, his obvious <u>interest</u> in the past and an ability to spot and <u>value</u> particular objects or 'triggers' to memory. However he's also contributing other skills: he has a <u>sensitivity</u> to the feelings and concerns of the people he's working with; he works as a carer and so needs to know about things such as special dietary needs when it comes to sharing round sweets; he's <u>aware</u> of the different ways impairments can affect how people take part in groups and reinforces and <u>responds</u> to everyone's contribution, making sure that everyone gets a hearing. These are <u>group management</u> skills. Gary also needs to know how to <u>communicate</u> what he does in the group to other workers at Millmead and to other people who may be in a position to determine if the reminiscence work is to continue to be resourced, so he needs to be able to demonstrate the outcomes of his work to his managers, Jane O'Leary and Mark Blake. At the same time he also needs to be able to <u>draw in</u> his fellow workers so that they also feel that this is care work and something they can contribute to. Finally, but not least, he needs to be able to convince the older people that what they are doing is valued and worthwhile. Quite a list of specifications in addition to his job as care co-ordinator!

I've underlined some key words in the feedback to this activity. You might like to go back to your own notes. Did you note down similar points which you could also highlight?

We're going to go on to look at some of these attributes and skills in more detail to see what they reveal about group management and the ways in which group life can contribute to a wider context of care and support.

We'll look at two issues: the need for support in groupwork, and whether what goes on in a reminiscence group can be described as therapy.

5.2 Support for groupwork

Support for the group also implies support for the group leader. In Activity 9 we saw that the Millmead group not only needed commitment from its members and its leader, it needed support from the rest of the staff if it was to achieve its aims.

It might seem that places where people are living or meeting on a daily or at least a regular basis form a natural environment for groupwork. Research suggests that this is not necessarily the case. For many people, living in a communal setting is a matter of maintaining privacy in a public setting, as we saw in Unit 8, and they may be unwilling to enter into activities which force them to say more than they want to about themselves or to spend more time than they would naturally choose to with other people they will be seeing all day long.

Sometimes, however, it is difficult to decide to what extent resistance to collective or shared activities is a defense against institutional living or the result of institutionalisation. In Unit 8 we read about the research which a team from the University of North London carried out in the 1980s. They visited over a hundred residential homes:

> *One of the strongest images of life in residential homes for the elderly is that of old people, relatively motionless, sitting around the walls of large sitting rooms. It has to be said that this image, unfortunately, is not ill-founded and that most residents do spend the larger part of the day gathered together in such lounges.*

> *(Kellaher et al., 1985, p. 44)*

More than 10 years later, there is still much evidence to suggest that this is not an unusual experience for frail older people living in residential care. Research carried out for Manchester City Council Social Services Department among older people living in residential care used group discussion to bring out residents' views of their living situations. 'Having things to do' was discussed in all 10 groups and among the comments made was one resident's description of her day:

> *You get up and get dressed and have breakfast. You sit. You get up and go to the toilet. You come back. You sit. You get up and have lunch. You sit. You get up and go to the toilet. You come back. You sit. You get up and have tea. You sit, you go to the toilet. You sit, you come back. You sit. You go to bed. You can't sleep because you are not tired.*

> *(Raynes, 1995, p. 8)*

The impact of institutional life on staff who may have a predominantly medicalised understanding of ageing also means that opportunities to break with routines are unlikely as staff concentrate on providing direct care or are discouraged from spending time talking with residents beyond what is needed to complete tasks such as feeding, bathing and dressing. You'll remember discussing the effects of institutionalisation on residents and staff in Unit 8 and particularly the work style of staff at the Cedar Court nursing home. It's possible to paint a bleak picture and there are clearly many exceptions. The role of the manager can be crucial to making a difference, as Mike Bender a psychologist who works with older people suggests. His '15 ways to lose your group' (see overleaf) have been drawn up to help care staff identify what can go wrong with reminiscence groups in settings where neither staff nor residents are helped to break out of oppressive routines. Though he's talking about a reminiscence group his list could apply to other types of groups set up in other settings by care workers or volunteers.

15 ways to lose your group

1   The senior staff do not really want a reminiscence group.

2   They do not realise what it entails.

3   They do not realise that their commitment must be for the life of the group.

4   There is no suitably quiet time and place or large enough space to run the group.

5   The group leaders do not have enough time to run the group.

6   The group leaders don't feel that they have enough time.

7   The other staff are not even neutral towards the group.

8   The group leaders may not understand the purpose of the group and what their role is.

9   The group leaders may not have the necessary skills.

10 The group leaders are not free to plan the groups and to run them.

11 Group members may not be carefully selected.

12 Those selected may not want to join the group.

13 There are no arrangements for when the group leaders are sick or on leave.

14 There is no plan for what happens at the end of the group.

15 There are no plans to train new staff in groupwork skills.

(Adapted from Bender, 1996, pp. 4–6)

Activity 10   **What counts for most in supporting groupwork?**

Allow about 10 minutes   Look back through the notes you made for Activity 9 and the comments I
made. Compare these with Bender's list. What do you think counts for
most in ensuring the success of a group in a unit such as Millmead? If
you're not sure you could use your own experience to come up with an
example.

Comment   I don't know what you thought, but looking at Millmead it seems that the
role of the manager is absolutely crucial. However good the group
leader is, however committed the members are, without support in the
form of resourcing and a generally encouraging ethos within the unit, the
life of the group is not likely to be either long or fulfilling for the
participants.

What we saw in the video was an experience of group activity which
appears to permeate several other group structures at Millmead: staff
groups, groups which cross the boundary of the unit into the community
and Millmead itself. The role of managers such as Jane O'Leary and Mark
Blake in supporting this work is clearly significant.

We've tried to present an example of what looks like good practice, but
would you do anything differently?

One of our course readers felt that the '15 ways' is 'really useful' but then
she asked, 'How does it fit into today's culture of effectiveness and
efficiency?' Perhaps she was pointing out how workers sometimes feel that
they have little choice when it comes to introducing good practice on their
own.

The activity room at Millmead

5.3 Engaging the staff group

Support from other members of staff is a theme which many
groupworkers and group members return to. Perhaps it's a question of
engaging with the staff as a group and finding ways to ensure their
support. This can be difficult if you are an outsider.

Gun Lewis was given an open remit to run group activities in a south east London residential home for older people. She found that her role as an 'outsider' presented problems. She had been given a goal: 'to encourage good care practice'. She describes her difficulties:

> *Quite frequently it is 'outsiders' who start a group and events in the establishment go on much as before. All sorts of activities are brought in and offered to residents, often with little active response apart from the staff having to persuade and cajole people to attend. The potential for staff to initiate and support groups within residential care settings is immense, but unfortunately so are the barriers. Groupwork is seen as extra and expert; to be done only if there is time and proven expertise available. 'Outsiders' are seen as people with both, care staff as people with neither. I had great difficulty managing to create and protect the time and space required to get the group going. It was seen by my colleagues as a luxury activity which they would like to happen but would have to take second place to the 'real work' of the place. Such pressure is on care staff all the time. It can be seen in their reluctance to sit still in social situations with residents, at breakfast, watching a favourite television programme, or just sitting and talking.*
>
> *(Lewis, 1992, p. 50)*

When she became an officer-in-charge, managing a 33-bed home, she saw things from the other side:

> *The very real pressure of low staff ratios, inflexible shift patterns and lack of finance are all difficulties which need overcoming. However, in my experience these are not the most insurmountable problems. Peer pressure on staff, their lack of confidence and limited perceptions of their job. although less tangible, are greater obstacles.*
>
> *(p. 56)*

She argues that for groupwork to succeed it should be seen to connect more obviously to life and work in a home but she also points out that:

> *Time and energy have to be invested to ensure staff gain the necessary confidence to embark on groupwork. Time must also be found to carry out the inevitable individual follow up work with residents as a result of experiences and changes occurring in groups. Time for staff supervision, continuous support and training has also to be found.*
>
> *(p. 57)*

Someone who commented on this part of the course noted that 'home grown' solutions to encouraging good care practice are much more likely to succeed if they are recognised and owned by the staff and group members too. He also suggested that groups of care staff need to develop 'maintenance work', their own form of groupwork, to keep up the interest and enthusiasm after the outside leader goes. Millmead is fortunate to have Gary Baker. Activities organisers who are staff members are still regarded as something of a luxury in many establishments.

There's another aspect of support which group leaders, particularly those working in areas like reminiscence, tend to refer to, and which can have an impact on the way a group works. This is the issue of supervision for the leader, as Lewis has pointed out. On the video Gary Baker mentions times when the group goes well. There are other times when things may not go to plan. There can be a whole variety of ways a group seems to 'fail'. It may be that a group member may be overwhelmed by emotions they cannot control. Sometimes it may be the leader who feels upset. While we were making the video I talked to Gary about his feelings as a group leader. He told me:

> *It's families that are the difficult thing aren't they? You have got to be very delicate like. I've been on several reminiscence sessions of mainly men which is quite upsetting. I must admit I've cried once or twice after what I've heard, and I wish I had someone I could go and chat to ... but I'm lucky because I'm in a network of two other friends who do reminiscence and we're all exchanging good ideas, and I normally say, 'Well I've had this happen today what do you think?' you know. And one of them's had counselling training and I think that helps.*

I asked him what he would do if he was 'getting in a bit deep with someone':

> *Seek further advice I think. Really talk about the problem ... obviously I wouldn't mention any names ... but you say, I've got this problem with a client, very distressed, then if they're badly distressed they need counselling, I think I'd refer it to the office, or the care manager. I'd be looking for support for the person and for the worker through groupwork of some kind.*

I also asked Mark Blake whether, as a manager, he could count on support for a group leader. He explained:

> *I think as an organisation, social services has ways of supporting its staff. If I wasn't able to give the support, I know I could find within the organisation a channel for that to be brought in, so we do have some back up. We're not left on our own to muddle through and I think with the knowledge we have within the establishment, we can find ways to support each other, and the clients.*

I was interested to know what support he might look for:

> *It would depend on the actual events or what's happened, but I mean there is a support line for Kent County Council staff which everybody is entitled to use and it's confidential so that's always there. I would certainly give the individuals, be it clients or staff, my time and I'm sure that would work its way throughout Canterbury and Thanet. You know we are a caring organisation so I think it's important that we show that we care to our staff as well as our clients.*

What Gary and Mark are both identifying are issues of staff burn out as well as boundaries. Engaging in groupwork can be stressful for reasons we've pointed out so far:

- it can expose workers to difficult emotions, their own as well as other people's
- it can raise issues of inadequacy if resources don't permit the work to be developed fully or appropriately
- it can cause problems within staff groups if there is resistance to what is being tried out.

Being able to talk in staff groups, to managers and, as a last resort, to the type of 'help line' that Mark mentions, is an important part of working with groups. Similarly, knowing where your responsibilities begin and end, establishing boundaries so that you know when and where to get help and support, is also important. Gary has managerial support, but he also says that he has developed his own group, a network of others who are also involved in reminiscence work, outside his particular work setting. Their additional expertise and backup provides him with emotional and practical support.

Talking it through with a more experienced colleague

Other workers have identified the need to talk to others and to get support and advice when involved in running groups. Brown and Mistry discuss the importance of having a 'same race' consultant for group leaders who encounter prejudice or discriminatory behaviour, quoting an example of a black woman worker jointly facilitating a group of white women bringing up children of mixed parentage. As the only black person in the group she encountered 'oppressive racism in the group ... such that although she had a racially aware and supportive white colleague she desperately needed to talk through what she was experiencing, on a one-to-one basis with a black consultant – quite separate from any consultancy for the workers as a pair' (1994, pp. 19–20). Brown identifies the need to be prepared to be open and to have the 'capacity for self-disclosure', particularly where personal feelings are involved in working with groups in residential and day care units. He argues that the more open someone is about the processes and their feelings that 'potentially high levels of support [will be] available on-the-spot from colleagues and supervisors' (Brown, 1990, p. 283).

5.4 Therapy or therapeutic?

A problem for some people stems from the claim which is sometimes made that what is going on in groups such as the Millmead group is 'therapy'. There seems to be a great deal of therapy about these days, with gardening, music, art – almost any activity – acquiring this label. Psychologists like Bender are clear that while they may be *therapeutic*, the activity in itself is not therapy. He draws a distinction:

> *Therapy, as commonly understood, occurs (1) when a person, commonly called the patient (2) perceives at some level that they have a problem and (3) is referred, or less commonly, refers themselves to a mental health specialist. (4) After an assessment, (5) the specialist and patient agree on a formulation of the patient's problems. (6) The therapist, selecting from a number of possible approaches or techniques ... (7) offers the most suitable one to the patient, who (8) consents.*

> *We can see that the usual reminiscence group fulfils none of these criteria. Most centrally, the member does not come believing he or she has a number of problems that the therapist will help them tackle. So, **does this mean reminiscence groupwork has no benefit**? Because reminiscence work is not therapy, this in no way implies that it is without benefit. Unfortunately, 'therapy' occupies the high ground of prestige, casting into shadow such usages as giving residents stimulation or activity; giving them one enjoyable hour a week to look forward to; building up cohesion in the group so that it can move into other purposes; rehabilitating communication and social skills etc.*

> *(Bender, 1994, p. 40)*

In reflecting on what had been happening in the groups he had led, he concludes:

> *I thought that if we knew that these were **not** therapy groups, then they could not look or feel like them. But what had happened was that we had created a setting, a structure in which the members felt safe and secure and felt able to manifest these factors – self-disclosure, acceptance, catharsis etc. Therapeutic effects were taking place.*

> *(Bender, 1994, p. 41)*

You'll remember that at the beginning of this unit we talked about the group run with adolescent girls at the hostel as having 'therapeutic aspects'. What Bender is suggesting is the need to recognise the positive outcomes of groupwork without imposing on group leaders or participants the responsibility for managing or achieving change in particular aspects of individual people's lives. If an awareness of a more deep-felt need is manifested in a group, then skilled professional help and supervision must be available.

Bender's warnings may feel rather imposing so let's leave the last word to Gary at Millmead. After we made the video I asked Gary how he felt the session went:

> *... now that the session's finished and they're having a cup of tea and they're winding down ... they'll be in the next room talking about school days which is part of the trick really, to make them do the talking rather than me being the prompt ... the idea is to make people aware of reminiscence, not to upset them. You know I wouldn't like to be doing reminiscence if it means they leave the room upset. That's not my aim. It's to give them a feeling of self-worth which I think they got today.*

Key points

- Everyone involved in groupwork will be contributing with some type of skill.

- Skills in groupwork include listening, accounting, supporting, communicating.

- Group leaders need support from managers and co-workers and opportunities for supervision.

- We need to be careful about using the term 'therapy' – groupwork may be helpful or therapeutic to members but does not involve assessing people as having problems and is not a form of treatment.

Section 6
Self-help groups

So far in this unit you've been looking at groups which have been organised by someone designated as a leader on the basis of their professional skills or their position in an organisation. These leaders may have shared many of the same experiences as the group members but their role and reason for taking part has been different. For one thing they may have been paid to be there, it may be part of the job of people like Gary Baker, Kavita Kohli and the staff at the girls' hostel, to organise and run groups. They will almost certainly have been trained or given some support in preparation for running the group and they will have ideas about what they want the group to achieve just by meeting, even if what develops is far from their original plans.

I'm ending the unit with a look at self-help groups. These are groups made up from people who usually share a common problem or are seeking a common goal. They are rooted in ideas of equality and shared experience and quite often deliberately seek not to involve professionals. But what makes them distinctive? Let's look at the following set of characteristics.

- *Their main purpose is to help and support members in dealing with their problems.*
- *They are begun and are controlled by the members themselves (though they may sometimes be initiated by workers who provide back up, a place to meet, publicity).*
- *Help comes from the skills and experience of the members themselves (though professional help may be called in if the group decides).*
- *The group is made up from people who share similar life experiences or problems.*
- *The group is run and controlled by its members (though they may sometimes ask for professional help or guidance).*

(Adapted from Levy, 1976, pp. 311–12)

Self-help is a particularly strong tradition within health care with groups forming around particular conditions or illnesses where people are able to give each other help, support and advice in dealing with some of the problems they are facing. But there have been other types of self-help too.

Activity 11   Where is self-help?

Allow about 5 minutes   You might like to pause for a moment and think about any self-help groups that you've noticed or perhaps joined yourself. Note down any that come to mind. If you can't think of any then next time you're at a doctor's surgery, health centre or community centre have a look at the notice board to see if any are advertising there. We've seen some examples already in K100. Are there any which spring to mind?

Comment   The groups I thought about were stroke groups, Alcoholics Anonymous, peer group counselling, carers' support groups. Sometimes national organisations like the Alzheimers' Disease Society support their own

Let's Face It
Support Network
Patron: Victoria Wood

for very special people
with faces to match

Claire Hart
(Trust Secretary)

Christine Piff
14 Fallowfield, Yateley,
Surrey GU17 7LW.
Tel: (01252) 879630
Fax: (01252) 872633

London Office: Tel/Fax (0181) 9312829

Registered Charity No. 1043461

MOEBIUS SYNDROME SUPPORT NETWORK

Mrs. Linda Anderson
21 Shields Road
Whitley Bay
Tyne & Wear
NE25 8UJ

Telephone & Fax:
(0191) 253 2090

TAMBA ADMINISTRATOR

Gina Siddons BA Cert Ed

PO Box 30
Little Sutton
South Wirral
L66 1TH

Tel/Fax: 0151 348 0020

Registered Charity No. 326734

Registered Charity No. 1000598

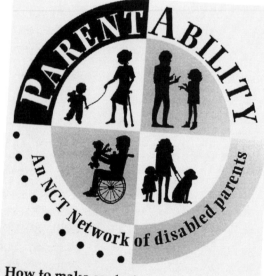

How to make contact.

You can contact us via the NCT's national office (24 hour answerphone). They will put you in touch with a member of ParentAbility who will deal with your enquiry.

The National Childbirth Trust offers information and support in pregnancy, childbirth and early parenthood, and aims to enable every parent to make informed choices. Donations to support the NCT are welcome.

Registered office
Alexandra House, Oldham Terrace,
Acton, London W3 6NH
Telephone: 081 992 8637

Registered number 2370537 (England)
Registered charity number 801395

Registered Charity No. 2370537

Contact: Beryl Washington
Meet-A-Mum Association (MAMA)
14 Willis Rod
Croydon
Surrey CR0 2XX
0181 665 6357

Registered Charity No. 283271

self-help groups. There are also groups like pensioners' groups, mothers and toddlers groups, set up to campaign or to provide a local service. Self-help groups obviously meet many different types of need.

The examples from the course that I thought of were the Parkinson's disease support group that Ruth Pinder mentions in Unit 2, Mrs Bright's carers' support group in Unit 7, Paul Theobald's HIV/AIDS self-support group in Unit 14 and Gary's informal support which he's built up for himself with other people who are engaged in reminiscence work with older people.

Self-help has developed at a great rate over the last 50 years or so. One study shows that in the USA the number of Alcoholics Anonymous groups alone increased from 50 in 1940 to 18,612 in 1972 (Tracy and Gussow, 1976, p. 383). Since the 1970s the women's movement has been particularly important to the development of self-help.

We've identified several different examples of self-help groups and noted some common characteristics. With so many to draw from as examples of self-help it might be useful to see if we can classify all this variety so that we can perhaps understand more about the reasons why self-help groups are set up and how they survive.

Activity 12   **Classifying self-help groups**

Allow about 30 minutes

Turn to Offprint 21. While reading, note the two headings Kelleher uses to classify self-help groups and define them in your own words. As you read on, note down some of the reasons why the groups he describes cross over between the two categories he identifies. Does this mean that the classification isn't useful?

Comment   Near the start of this excerpt Kelleher distinguishes 'inner-focused' and 'outer-focused' self-help groups. By 'inner-focused' he seems to mean groups whose members are more concerned with how they feel, understanding each other and sharing problems. By 'outer-focused' I think he means groups which seek to represent members' interests to outside organisations or authorities.

Having set up this classification he then goes on to show how the groups he cites as examples are both 'inner' and 'outer' focused. This is because, as he explains it:

- groups may be set up by professionals yet their members also seek to share experience – for example the National Ankylosing Spondylitis Society (NASS)

- groups may start as inner-focused but may become outer-focused if the members begin to explain their situation in terms of external rather than personal problems – for example the women members of the local TRANX group who began to criticise the ways doctors gave out tranquillisers

- some organisations may include both types of group so that members gain the benefit of both forms of self-help activity – for example the British Diabetic Association includes groups with pressure and information seeking activities as well as groups set up to provide personal support and advice from other people with diabetes.

Is the classification of 'inner' and 'outer' useful? The point about a classification is that it helps us to identify main characteristics and if there is no clear 'fit' then to try to explain why. It is a basis from which to begin an analysis. The two categories of 'inner' and 'outer' can be used not just to differentiate one self-help group from another, they also help us to see how a group might change its focus over time, or may be compromised by the interests of more powerful groups. In the case of the NASS, for example, the involvement of professionals meant that some of the 'inner' type activities tended not to be developed.

Self-help groups play an important part in providing support and sharing information. They are part of the web of organisations and roles which together make up our health and social care structures. In their own way they can support paid carers by maintaining networks of contact and communication between service users. Feeding back ideas and experience, members of self-help groups can contribute to better quality services, responding more immediately to specific needs.

Self-help groups have had their critics. They've been seen as limited by the range of skills and experience of their members. Without external, professional or additional skills there's a danger that they can't move on and develop. They may get stuck at a particular stage particularly if they come to be valued mainly for the emotional support they give to the individuals who make it up. They may find it difficult to accept new members. They may be seen as substituting for paid services. Some self-help groups are run by patients, carers and service users because there is no alternative provided. This might be the case for some support groups and information services which in earlier times might have been provided with budgets and a member of staff to work with them. And, being groups, they are susceptible to all the limitations which ordinary groups can be prey to. Despite their apparent equality and sharing basis, they are just as likely to be affected by inequalities of power rooted in differences of class, ethnicity and gender, and they may find it difficult to manage relationships with professionals and facilitators who, ultimately, may or may not choose to listen to their message.

I asked someone whose partner has cancer to write about her experience of a self-help group.

> *I think there were three reasons why self-help didn't seem right in this situation. Firstly, I didn't want to acknowledge that I needed help ... this was a club that I definitely did not want to belong to [people whose partners have cancer]. I kept hoping the diagnosis would go away ... and anyway 'our' cancer was different from, in turn less serious than, and then more serious than, rarer than ... everyone else's. I did not want other people's experiences to either amplify my fears about what was happening to our family or diminish them, to confirm or confront the scenarios we were grappling with.*

> *Secondly, there was an ideological fault line. Perhaps I was a bit paranoid but I detected beneath the New Age jargon more than a hint of victim blaming. The emphasis on taking vitamins, relaxing, changing lifestyle and so on can seem like an accusation as well as a remedy. It is as if someone is saying if you had been living right this wouldn't have happened ... I knew my partner had been living healthily, and I grew to resent this notion that what had gone wrong was somehow under his control. This is not to dismiss the importance of keeping healthy through treatment but I knew this might not be enough and couldn't abide the 'crystals at dawn' gung-ho evangelicism.*

Lastly, by the time I got round to acknowledging that we did need help, we had lost two close friends through cancer on top of the strain of dealing with my partner's illness, and I felt too depleted. Self-help groups work by being reciprocal and I did not want to pay the entrance fee of feeling obliged to help other people too. I needed to be looked after at this stage without having to give anything back for a while ... I did not have anything to give. I had started to feel overwhelmed by outside demands, I was shutting out bits of the outside world I couldn't cope with, forgetting things, withdrawing to regroup. I was referred to a bereavement counsellor at the local hospice and have found the professional help invaluable. My counsellor has been able to give me the benefit of a lot of other people's experience at one remove, and to lead me to practical ways of coping and making decisions which mobilise our particular resources in the face of continued uncertainty.

This was clearly not a positive experience. Not all the reasons she gives can necessarily be attributed to self-help as such, the 'New Age' jargon for example. However, it does seem that for some people, group-based *self*-help may be less appropriate than individualised professionally-based support.

Much of the interest in self-help particularly in relation to health care, as the article by Kellaher suggests, is that it helps lay people to become more confident about the decisions which they make about their own health and strategies for care. Some professionals see them as complementary to their own work, encouraging patients to become more assertive and self-confident through talk and discussion. Finally, Kellaher suggests that doctors' own prescribing practice may benefit from what they learn from the activities of self-help groups.

I'll leave the last word to someone who is a survivor of childhood sexual abuse and who gave us this account of a group to which she belonged for a number of years:

Being in a self-help group for adult women survivors of childhood sexual abuse was a major part of healing for me. It was as if I had suddenly discovered that I had previously been speaking a foreign language and now I was speaking my own native tongue and being understood effortlessly. The experience was overwhelming at times – I didn't have to hide anything, translate my way of thinking into 'normal' before speaking or avoid saying 'odd ' things that other people didn't understand – and no one was fooled either. If I closed down and said I was fine they knew I wasn't. In time I felt more and more whole in other parts of my life as I came to understand just what the effects of being a survivor in our society were – the others in the group were like mirrors. I also recognised my own strength and courage through seeing theirs and identifying with them. In the group we could explore boundaries and experiment relatively safely with intimacy, we could support each other in bringing about change and most of all we came to understand ourselves through understanding each other. I no longer felt isolated and I realised that I was not wrong in being different, but that my differences of perception and understanding were a direct consequence of having had to deal not only with the actual events of my childhood, but just as much with the denial and rejection of the society as a whole. Self-help groups are an important feature of the survivor network as a whole – they are not always successful, but many survivors [of childhood sexual abuse] have found them a positive and healing experience as I did.

Key points

- Self-help groups tend to be made up from people who share a common problem or goal; they are based on ideals of sharing and support.

- Some self-help groups may have been set up by professionals as a way of enabling service users to express their feelings and 'get things off their chest'.

- Some professionals see self-help groups as a necessary complement to their own skills.

- Self-help groups may be just as prey to the problems and challenges that face conventional groups.

Study skills: Self-help study groups

Your needs as a student are not of the same order as the groups we have been discussing. Nevertheless the concept of the 'self-help group' has been much used in the OU. Perhaps you have formed a group with fellow K100 students – if not, perhaps you still could – especially with the summer weeks ahead when tutorials are scarce, and with the exam beyond that, when mutual help can be a great boon. Look back quickly over the points made in Section 6 and see how far they can be applied to self-help groups in a study context.

Conclusion

In this unit we've looked at group experiences. We began with definitions of groups and then looked at some particular experiences of groupwork. We looked at what goes on when people remember together and what this can tell us about how groups work and what goes on in groups.

We then went on to look at ways in which groups can sometimes exclude people and discussed some strategies for dealing with difference, including groups based in sameness as well as self-help groups. We looked at the sorts of skills and knowledge which participating in a group involves and the importance of supervision and support. We identified factors which enable us to describe what goes on in groups as therapeutic.

Whether you see yourself as a group member, a group facilitator, a group observer, or perhaps all three, you probably recognised different group reactions, strategies and activities that you may have taken part in. Drawing on your own experience and the experience of the people we have featured in the course so far is an important aspect of your work for K100. Fitting that experience to ideas, models and theories of how people behave and relate to one another is an essential complement to that process. In Unit 16 we continue with experience and theorising but adding an extra dimension: time. Adding time as a dimension enables us to broaden our comparisons and diversify our sources of information. It also provides us with a measure against which to place our own explanations and experience in health and social care.

Study skills: Day schools

I have mentioned tutorials as examples of 'groups', but day schools (which may form part of K100 provision in your OU region) are also group events. The differences are that they are:

- more fleeting, so group processes cannot develop very far
- larger scale, so group processes are more impersonal.

Nevertheless the group processes are important. You can have a day school that feels friendly and supportive, or one where you feel like an outsider. You can also make very valuable contact with people even if you never meet them again. A few minutes in a small group discussion can open up other people to you surprisingly quickly.

Day schools may also offer the opportunity to participate in a different kind of group – where you play the role of 'member of an audience', as someone gives a talk. This form of study, which you seldom meet in K100, is of course a central experience of students in conventional courses – and it demands particular skills. Although it is not central in K100, it is worth developing some of the skills. So, bearing in mind any experiences at day schools, read Section 3 of Chapter 3 of *The Good Study Guide*.

Study diary

Finally, a reminder half way through the block to consider what might be useful to put in your study diary.

References

Atkinson, D. (1994) ' "I got put away" Group-based reminiscence with people with learning difficulties' in Bornat, J. (ed.) *Reminiscence Reviewed: Perspectives, Evaluations, Achievements*, Open University Press, Buckingham.

Bender, M. (1994) 'An interesting confusion: what can we do with reminiscence groupwork?' in Bornat, J. (ed.) *Reminiscence Reviewed: Perspectives, Evaluations, Achievements*, Open University Press, Buckingham.

Bender, M. (1996) '15 ways to lose your group: reminiscence groups – when they go wrong: why', *Reminiscence*, Vol. 13, pp. 4–6.

Brown, A. (1979) *Groupwork*, Heinemann, London.

Brown, A. (1990) 'The group "mosaic" in residential and day care settings', *Groupwork*, Vol. 3, No. 3, pp. 269–85.

Brown, A. and Mistry, T. (1994) 'Group work with "mixed membership" groups: issues of race and gender', *Social Work with Groups*, Vol. 15, No. 3, pp. 5–21.

Buchanan, K. and Middleton, D. (1995) 'Voices of experience: talk, identity and membership in reminiscence groups', *Ageing and Society*, Vol. 15, No. 4, pp. 457–91.

Campbell, J. and Oliver, M. (1996) *Disability Politics: Understanding Our Past, Changing Our Future*, Routledge, London.

Douglas, T. (1976) *Groupwork Practice*, Tavistock, London.

Francis-Spence, M. (1994) 'Groupwork and Black women viewing networks as groups: Black women meeting together for affirmation and empowerment', *Groupwork*, Vol. 7, No. 2, pp. 109–16.

Gibson, F. (1992) 'Reminiscence groupwork with older people', *Groupwork*, Vol. 5, No. 3, pp. 28–40.

Harris, J. and Hopkins, T. (1994) 'Beyond anti-ageism: reminiscence groups and the development of anti-discriminatory social work education and practice' in Bornat, J. (ed.) *Reminiscence Reviewed: Perspectives, Evaluations, Achievements*, Open University Press, Buckingham.

Kellaher, L.A., Peace, S.M. and Willcocks, D.M. (1985) *Living in Homes: A Consumer View of Old People's Homes*, Centre for Environmental and Social Services in Ageing (CESSA), Department of Applied Social Studies, Polytechnic of North London, and the British Association for Service to the Elderly (BASE).

Kent County Council Social Services Department, Canterbury and Thanet Area (1995) *The Business Plan for Thanet Elderly Service Provision Group*, 1995–6.

Kohli, K. (1993) 'Groupwork with deaf people', *Groupwork*, Vol. 6, No. 3, pp. 232–47.

Levy, L.H. (1976) 'Self-help groups: types and psychological processes', *Journal of Applied Behavioural Science*, Vol. 12, No. 3, pp. 310–22.

Lewis, G. (1992) 'Groupwork in a residential home for older people', *Groupwork*, Vol. 5, No. 1.

Lewisham West Reminiscence Group (1993) *Harmonious Reminiscences: Memories of Black Elders Coming to Lewisham*, Lewisham Social Services.

Milson, F. (1973) *An introduction to Groupwork Skill*, Routledge and Kegan Paul, London.

Payne, M. (1991) *Modern Social Work Theory*, Macmillan, London.

Raynes, N.V. (1995) *Standard Setting in Residential and Nursing Homes, Report on Phase 1*. Prepared for Manchester City Council Social Services Department, University of Huddersfield.

Rice, S. and Goodman, C. (1992) 'Support groups for older people: is homogeneity or heterogeneity the answer?', *Groupwork*, Vol. 5, No. 2, pp. 65–77.

Ryan, T. and Walker, R. (1993) *Life Story Work*, British Agencies for Adoption and Fostering, London.

Sprott, W.J.H. (1952) *Social Psychology*, Methuen, London.

Tracy, S.G. and Gussow, Z. (1976) 'Self-help health groups: a grass-roots response to a need for services', *Journal of Applied Behavioural Science*, Vol. 12, No. 3, pp. 381–96.

Tuckman, B.W. (1965) 'Developmental sequences in small groups', *Psychological Bulletin*, 63, pp. 384–99.

Acknowledgements

Grateful acknowledgement is made to the following sources for permission to reproduce material in this unit:

Illustrations

Pp. 60 and 96: John Birdsall Photography; *pp. 69 and 71*: Courtesy of Kent County Council Social Services; *p. 77:* Copyright Jeni McKenzie/ mckenzie heritage picture archive; *p. 80:* Chapeltown Black Women Writers' Group (1992) *When Our Ship Comes In - Black Women Talk*, Yorkshire Art Circus. Cover Design © Tadpole Graphics; *p. 85*: Courtesy of Asian Women's Group at Leicester Centre for Deaf People; *p. 100 (top left):* Courtesy of Let's Face It; *p. 100 (top centre):* Courtesy of Moebius Syndrome Support Network; *p. 100 (top right):* Courtesy of Twins and Multiple Births Association; *p. 100 (centre left):* Courtesy of Support After Murder and Manslaughter; *p. 100 (bottom left):* Courtesy of Meet-a-Mum Association; *p. 100 (bottom right):* Courtesy of the National Childbirth Trust.

Unit 16
Recounting the past

Prepared for the course team by Joanna Bornat

While you are working on Unit 16, you will need:
- Course Reader
- Offprints Book
- *The Good Study Guide*
- Block 4 video part 2, 'Lennox Castle Hospital: a hidden history'
- Care in the UK
- Wallchart

Contents

Introduction

In this unit we are going to look at the different ways of finding out about how care was provided and how people experienced care in the past. In doing this we will look at the history of one particular type of care: institutional care. We're doing this because:

- institutional care has played a very big part in the history of care. It has also had a strong influence on how care is understood. Policies about residential care have often influenced how needs for care are defined, how forms of treatment are developed and certainly how people have experienced receiving care

- finding out about the past means developing *skills of observation, recording, listening and communicating*. These are research skills which are relevant not just for exploring the past but for finding out generally: searching, investigating and communicating evidence and experience. Research skills like these are not just for historians, they are helpful when it comes to developing sensitive care policies, helping people to cope with change in their lives – research skills are also good working-with-people skills.

In Unit 8 we looked at what happens when people live collectively in institutions today. We considered ways of safeguarding quality of life and maintaining independence and individuality in residential settings. Some attempts at solutions to questions about how best to manage living and working in an institution have emerged from years of experience of that form of care provision. Similarly, debates about whether or not institutional care is always appropriate also have a long history.

Core questions

- How is research into the past helpful to an understanding of the experience and practice of care today?

- What kinds of evidence are available to someone who wants to find out about the past?

- To what extent are the skills of a researcher also appropriate when working with people and providing help and support?

Thomas Coram's Foundling Hospital, Richard Wilson, pictured in 1746

To explore these issues in more detail this unit takes as a case study the history of one institution set up for people with learning difficulties in the 1920s. We've chosen this particular topic because it's likely that by the early years of the twenty-first century those great institutions of the eighteenth, nineteenth and twentieth centuries – the asylums and mental handicap hospitals – will have ceased to exist. Early developments like the Foundling Hospital of Thomas Coram in London opened in 1742 were later followed by an extensive period of building which resulted in the Victorian asylums including workhouses, prisons and, for children, the type of residential 'district school' that Charlie Chaplin experienced at the 'Lambeth Union Institution for Boys', as well as children's homes run by charities such as Barnardo's and the Church of England's Waifs and Strays Society. This programme continued well into the twentieth century with the construction of large-scale complexes designed for people with learning difficulties as we shall see later.

By the year 2000, 98 of the remaining 121 large mental hospitals in the UK were scheduled to have closed. As the community care policies of the 1980s and 1990s work their way through, those landmarks of care and control will scarcely be recognisable. Depending on their age and significance in terms of 'heritage', these buildings will have been pulled down and replaced by low cost housing or offices, others are destined to be converted into exclusive dwellings, supermarkets, nursing homes or public open space.

For some people the destruction of the buildings is a devastating blow to 'the nation's public heritage':

> *... these are buildings on which the Victorians lavished pride and money. The Royal Holloway Sanatorium has interior finishes as rich as the House of Lords – as* The Builder *noted at the time. St Francis, Haywards Heath is a composition as powerful as the Natural History Museum in the Cromwell Road.*

> *The first mental hospital, Bethlehem, had been built by Dr Robert Hooke – one of Wren's most talented contemporaries. The tradition of fine architecture continued with John Carr at York. During the nineteenth century most lunatic asylums were the subject of architectural competitions attracting new talent and new ideas.*

> *Above all these asylums represent a classic English marriage of well proportioned architecture, splendid landscape grounds and fine views across the country around.*

It would be easy to say disparagingly that the Victorians simply wanted to push the asylums out of sight. But this argument does not hold up. Many were built in large leafy grounds in, or adjacent to, Victorian suburbia. Examples are St Andrew's in Northampton and Friern in Barnet near Alexandra Palace, London.

Second, where hospitals are set in open country they are given prime sites on south facing slopes with good views. I have seen none in bad positions with unattractive neighbours. These are the kind of sites architects or landscape designers would have chosen for the most imposing stately homes.

(Binney, 1995, p. 1)

PROPERTY EXPRESS

Shot in the arm for former hospitals

The closure of hospitals, although considered bad news by most, has at least had an upside for property developers. Two ambitious projects in Hampstead mean that, far from being in short supply, hospital beds in this area have never been more widely available.

Former hospital Mount Vernon is a mixed development of newly built and restored buildings, containing apartments and penthouses ranging in price from £275,000 for a one-bedroom, one reception room flat to £1,175,000 for four bedrooms and a double reception, through Knight Frank (0171-431-8686). There is also one separate six-bedroom detached residence.

Set in three areas [sic] of mixed formal gardens and parkland, architecturally, the development offers everything from Victorian fantasy in the turrets of Gainsborough House, which has been reconstructed within the original shell, to the stylish modernism of The Pavilions, a cascade of houses newly built into the hillside.

Mount Vernon House itself is a Queen Anne listed building restored to its former glory to provide six bedrooms, a double garage and a studio house within its own private grounds.

Anyone who buys in the scheme, jointly developed by

Mount Vernon has both new and restored buildings in a range of architectural styles

Marylebone Warwick Balfour and Sincere, will be offered a range of amenities, including membership of a health club, swimming pool, gym and sauna, on-site porterage and underground parking.

A second resuscitated hospital is at New End, now Upper Hampstead Walk, where existing Victorian buildings, like the 1884 Grade II-listed Rotunda, which has been converted into six spectacular semi-circular apartments, have been enhanced with newly built houses and apartments very much in keeping with the original buildings on site.

Apparently, one buyer has bought two of the apartments back-to-back and has hired an interior designer to decorate his new, completely circular home.

Prices range from £255,000 for

a two-bedroom apartment with high ceilings and long, dramatic windows in Giles' Building to around £470,000 for a terraced three-bed townhouse in Young's Row (still under construction).

Two of the six three-bedroom houses and showhouse are still available at Streatly Place, a charming, cottage-style row of homes built on what was the old hospital laundry and this part of the development will also incorporate a nursery for local children at the far end of the terrace.

The landmark chimney tower is also being retained and is currently being considered for Grade II listing.

(Hampstead and Highgate Express, 7 February 1997)

If the only remaining value of such buildings is their price in terms of land and architectural 'heritage' and if the policies which led to their construction have been superseded, why should finding out about them be of importance to understanding health and social care today? What's the point of 'raking up the past'? I started the unit by saying that knowing about the past is important as a way of measuring and accounting for change and continuity.

As you work through the unit you'll almost certainly come up with your own opinions about why history is important, but at this point I'm suggesting:

- there is a need to recognise that these buildings and the policies that led to the care regimes they housed are part of all our lives and experiences, however distant and separate they may seem

- history highlights the differences and the continuities between past and present: the buildings may be disappearing, but it isn't just buildings that lead to various kinds of behaviour, it's also the people who manage them and the policies they operate with

- there is a need to acknowledge and identify the 'hidden histories' of the people who lived in these buildings because they can tell us something about the consequences of such care policies in human terms – that's another way of asking if life inside matched up to the outside glories of the landscape and the architecture

- finding out about the past means learning how to ask the right sort of questions, where to find evidence and how to evaluate what we find, not just in relation to the written records which are left behind, and the bricks and mortar of buildings, but if possible from the people who lived and worked there and for whom institutions were a form of community life

- looking back to the past provides us with the opportunity to make comparisons and reflect on policies, practice and values today.

But if we want to look back to the history of care what kind of information do we have access to? Let's briefly look at three examples: personal experience, documents and photographs.

Section 1
Making a start on finding out

I've chosen three examples to show the potential and the limitations of different kinds of information about the past:

- personal experience
- documents
- photographs.

1.1 Personal experience

People's own memories and experience give clues where there may not be much left to see of past forms of health and social care provision.

Activity 1 | **Triggering our own memories**

Allow about 5 minutes | Think back on your own life. When did you first become aware of large asylums or mental handicap hospitals? Did they play a part in your community, or perhaps influence your own family's life? If they didn't, why do you think this was?

Comment | Some people go through life unaware of their nearest asylum or mental handicap hospital. Though some were built within city suburbs, many were built far from the large conurbations. And though these institutions dominated the landscape they tended to be highly self-contained, difficult to get into and difficult to get out of.

Other people live in communities where the local long-stay hospital is the main employer of labour. Family members may have worked there for generations. Then there are families with a member who may have lived for many years as a hospital patient; sometimes this has meant regular and frequent visiting, sometimes not.

Younger people today may have no knowledge at all that such hospitals ever existed. In some cases they've disappeared from the map. Earlier generations of children may have known about them more as a threat. In North London, they might be told they'd 'end up in Colney Hatch', in Newcastle on Tyne it was Cox Lodge and in Walsall a mother might say 'you'll have me in Burntwood' if you didn't behave. One of our course testers remembered that: 'The Retreat, York, is some 19 miles from where I've always lived and I have childhood memories of it being somewhere you never went'.

My own memory is of growing up in the 1950s between two large hospitals in the north east of England, one a mental handicap hospital (for people with learning difficulties) the other a 'mental hospital' (providing psychiatric treatment). Occasionally someone might escape and pass us as we played in the fields and woods. More frequently we saw groups of patients from the mental handicap hospital being taken for walks or to work in the fields. As a child I could see that they looked different from other grown ups. They seemed very shy. The women wore ankle socks, their clothes didn't look very smart, and the men and women walked separately in a crocodile along the road, sometimes holding each other's hands. I liked to go to visit a friend who lived at St George's, the mental hospital, where her father worked, because there was plenty of tarmac and concrete for roller-skating around her house.

The problem with my memories is that they are very much an outsider's account. If I really wanted to know more about these particular institutions I would need to talk to other people who lived and worked there. I would need to find out about how these hospitals were first set up, how big they were and how they were organised. That would mean reading up from official accounts and reports.

1.2 Documents

The history of St George's, Morpeth, is described in a report produced by SAVE Britain's Heritage. What does it tell us about this particular hospital?

> *The County Pauper Lunatic Asylum for Northumberland was built on a 99 acre site bought from the Earl of Carlisle from 1853 to 1859. It was designed in the Italianate style by Henry Welch and the Commissioners accepted a tender of £28,263 in October 1853 but the final cost was £82,000. The hospital was initially small, consisting of a superintendent's house and ward wings either side to detach male from female. The farm buildings and cottages were only completed in 1877 and the chapel in 1884 at which time more extensions were also added onto the main building including two new wings, a dining room, kitchen and administration block. When St George's opened it was designed for 200 patients though in its first year 1859 it accepted only 154. By 1868 this had risen to 143 males and 150 females. The initial acreage of the site was supplemented in various stages but by 1923 the land mass covered 243 acres with two infirmaries, an isolation hospital and various cottages. The buildings are mostly two storey of brick on an ashlar faced basement with stone quoins. The administration block has good quality fixtures and decoration and originally contained the superintendent's house.*

> *The Castle Morpeth Local Plan has allocated a section south of the main hospital for 150 houses as the hospital is set to close this year [1995]. To*

Male patients and attendants in front of the County Pauper Asylum, Morpeth, photograph taken c. 1900

the north of the Victorian buildings there is land for possible use by developers but which is sided by land designated as of 'high landscape value'. The core of the site is to be retained for residential or preferably business use with an improved A197 access road. The commitment to the retention of the buildings is weak and an Inner Morpeth Link road, which could drive straight through the core of the Victorian buildings, has only just been dropped.

(Binney, 1995, p. 30)

Reports like this obviously draw on other sources of evidence, like details about how much the hospital cost to build and how many people it was originally designed to take. However, reading it through still left me feeling that I wanted to know more about what it might be like to be a patient in, say, the 1880s, or what sort of people worked in such a hospital in those days. How did people come to be admitted in the first place and did they ever get better and return home?

1.3 Photographs

Photographs are another source of information. Let's look at this photograph taken of staff and patients at another hospital, Littlemore, at Oxford.

Patients and staff at Littlemore Hospital, Oxford, early 1900s

Activity 2 **What can we learn from a photograph?**

Allow about 5 minutes In the photograph above, male staff and patients in the early 1900s are posing for the camera. Littlemore was built as the 'Oxford County Pauper Lunatic Asylum' and opened in 1846. Its closure was marked 150 years later by the publication of a short history which included stories and images from its past. The photograph is one of many collected for the book (Goddard, 1996). This is an unusual photograph in many ways. What does it tell you about the life of a patient or a nurse at the beginning of the twentieth century and what questions does it raise for you?

Comment   This is strictly a group of *men* – patients and carers. Though it's difficult to
            tell with a black and white photograph, everyone seems to be wearing
            some kind of uniform. The nurses, or attendants as they were called, have
            two styles of cap, both of which have a vaguely military, or at any rate
            custodial, style. The men have identical suits with waistcoats, but no ties.
            Those that aren't bald have their hair cut very short.

            As for questions, what occurred to me first was how a black man came to
            be a patient in the hospital at a time when few black people lived in
            Oxfordshire, or even in Britain. How long had he, or indeed any of the
            patients in this picture, been living at Littlemore and why were they still
            there? Who were they, what were their names? Some of the men seem to
            be quite old. What kind of treatment had they had over the years? Did they
            have visitors or contact with their families? Who were the attendants and
            would they have needed different caring skills in those days before drugs
            came in? The cats also raise interesting issues about their place in the
            lives of the patients. And of course, there's no information about how or
            why this photograph came to be taken at all or who the photographer was.
            For a variety of reasons it was not common for patients in hospitals such
            as Littlemore to have their photographs taken.

            Photographs are full of detailed information but we may need documents
            or the opportunity to talk to people if we are going to be able to decode
            what we see.

It seems as if these different kinds of evidence about the past can't
answer enough of our questions. In what follows we're going to look at
one particular investigation and consider some of the issues which
looking back into the past raises for health and social care.

Key points

- Knowing about the past helps us to understand continuities
  and changes and to reflect on our own practices, policies and
  values today.

- Finding out about the past means having access to varied
  sources of information including documents, photographs
  and people's own experience.

Section 2
Lennox Castle Hospital: a twentieth century institution

In this section we follow through some of the issues we've just been considering with Howard Mitchell who has made a special study of Lennox Castle Hospital, about ten miles from Glasgow at Lennoxtown. His study is the subject of the second part of the video that accompanies this block. Lennox Castle Hospital belongs to the period of the 1920s and 1930s when separate provision for people with learning difficulties was being developed following the 1913 Mental Deficiency Act. You might find it useful at this point to turn to the wallchart to locate that Act. Lennox Castle was typical of large institutions built by local authorities in the 1930s and was the largest in the UK. At the time it opened it was considered to be 100 years ahead of its time by specialists visiting from the USA. Since then Lennox Castle has become well known as an example of a particular type of provision characterised by its isolation and by a certain notoriety among members of the public and nursing profession.

2.1 Finding out about Lennox Castle

Lennox Castle represented a large investment by the Corporation of Glasgow, who bought the land and built the hospital. But only 60 years after it was opened it was scheduled for closure. There was a need to capture and record life there before it, and the people associated with it, disappeared. But how did Howard Mitchell go about his research, and what did he find? You'll find out by watching the second part of the video: 'Lennox Castle Hospital: a hidden history'.

Activity 3   **Lennox Castle Hospital: what kind of an institution?**

Allow about 1 hour

Get ready to look at part 2 of the video. Don't worry if you feel you need to watch the video through more than once. This part lasts about 30 minutes. Watching a video when you're learning is different from watching for entertainment. You can use every bit or parts of it. You should make it work for *you* so use the pause button or rewind as much as you want to.

While you watch note down any words which come into your head about what kind of place Lennox Castle Hospital might have been to live or work in.

Comment   I don't know what words occurred to you, but what I noted down were adjectives like:

'safe'	'cruel'
'isolated'	'boring'
'frightening'	'caring'
'cold' (in the winter)	'oppressive'
'dangerous'	'inhuman'
'peculiar'	'stultifying'
'extraordinary'	'depressing'
'controlling'	

Someone who read this material suggested nouns like, 'friends and enemies', 'sharing', 'trust and distrust', 'fear', 'punishments and rewards'.

I didn't seem to come up with many positive words even though I saw people laughing and smiling about things they remembered. The story on the video evokes a mixture of emotions and it's difficult to know if people who lived and worked there share the same feelings about the place. Someone like James Lappin sounds quite resigned to life at the hospital, making the best of what he's had. When Colin Sproul talks about his work as a nurse, he's both bitter and realistic when he recalls the system he had to work with. There's something rather similar in both their attitudes. Margaret Scally remembers good times at the hospital, at work, but she leaves us with no illusions, she's pleased not to be there any longer. And Howard Mitchell, how does he come over? How well did you feel he coped with having been a nurse and with what he now knows as a researcher?

The hospital and the system it represents appear to be something of an enigma. But perhaps it's too easy to see it as extraordinary and isolated. Whatever our reactions, we need to be able to explain what we saw and to draw conclusions from it.

2.2 Explaining what we find out

How do we make sense of what we saw? The video tells the story of the hospital in dramatic tones: we hear about a riot, escapes, punishment and drug treatment regimes. But we also hear about football matches, dances and friendships. Even so, they are only part of the story of 60 years and many hundreds of people's lives. We saw several volumes of detailed records. What can be learnt from so much information? How can Howard Mitchell begin to organise all these facts and accounts?

One way of beginning is by drawing out some common themes from all the available evidence – the written and recorded data. Perhaps fortunately for us, we've only got the video to draw on, so let's start with that.

In Unit 8 you were introduced to Erving Goffman's ideas about institutional life. Here you are going to get an opportunity to use his model in relation to an example of the 'total institution' for which he became so well known. You'll remember that in Unit 8 you were presented with a summary of Goffman's four characteristics of institutional life. These were:

- **Batch living** – where people are treated as a homogeneous group without the opportunity for personal choice. Activity is undertaken *en masse*. Rules and regulations dominate and residents are watched over by staff.

- **Binary management** – where the two worlds of residents and staff are seen to be totally separate and staff wield power over residents by maintaining distance between them.

- **The inmate role** – where people who come to live in institutions are stripped of their former roles, made to break with the past, lose their personal identity and become an inmate.

- **The institutional perspective** – over time the inmate may come to accept the loss of self and the power of the institution, taking on roles which reinforce its existence.

Goffman also suggests that 'total institutions' are 'symbolised by the barrier to social intercourse with the outside world and to departure that is often built right into the physical plant, such as locked doors, high walls, barbed wire, cliffs, water, forests or moors' (Reader Chapter 8).

Lennox Castle Hospital main building and aerial view of the whole site

Activity 4   **Lennox Castle: a 'total institution'?**

Allow about 30 minutes   Taking each of Goffman's four characteristics note down some examples from what you saw in the video against each. How helpful is Goffman's model do you think? Does it fit completely onto the picture of Lennox Castle?

    At this point you may feel you need to watch the video again, particularly if you only watched it through once for Activity 3.

Comment   I don't know what you decided to enter under the four headings but here are a few examples which I felt fitted Goffman's model very well:

- **Batch living**. From what James, Margaret and Colin told us there was regimentation and a feeling that lives were lived out in very public conditions. Margaret mentioned the way clothes were handed out and Colin can still recite menus from nearly 60 years before. The detailed records of so much of people's lives suggest a public accountability concerned to establish that formal rules about behaviour and treatment were to be maintained whatever the cost to human dignity and individuality. Management of behaviour through drugs might also be viewed in this way.

- **Binary management**. Although we heard how staff lived on the hospital grounds and were subject to rigid supervision of their social lives there was plenty of evidence of the kind of separation which enabled staff to use physical and other powers over patients. Records were a form of control which were not open to patients to amend or contest and personal lives were subject to close scrutiny and observation. There were other separations within the hospital. The nursing staff had less power and access to information in comparison with the medical staff. Not so much a binary system perhaps, rather a hierarchy of divisions with the patients very much at the bottom.

- **The inmate role**. People like James and Margaret were very young when they first came into hospital. They learned how to grow up as inmates and seemed to have become skilled at living as patients at Lennox Castle. The inmate role was created from a range of what would have seemed extraordinary practices if anyone had attempted to impose them on people outside the hospital. Disability resulted in what sound like conditions more appropriate for prisons or military barracks. Reality seems to have been stood on its head: cruelties are defined as right and appropriate and defenceless people are defined as dangerous and immoral. Contacts with the outside world were strictly limited and regimented as the 'Regulations regarding the visiting of patients' (see opposite) make clear.

- **The institutional perspective**. This was perhaps less obvious from the video. Margaret Scally has moved out of the hospital and is obviously pleased to be able to distance herself physically and emotionally from the place. She also suggests that she never completely accepted the regime. Though she never ran away she says she wanted to. James Lappin comes over as someone who is more accepting and unquestioning of rules which meant that he and his girlfriend were never free to meet on their own.

Goffman's definition of a total institution might have been based on Lennox Castle. The hospital's layout, its grounds and its distance from most people's homes in Glasgow and further afield helped to contain everyone who lived and worked there. Everything seemed to be catered for. We heard about 'escapes' so presumably there was a feeling of barriers with the outside world that people tried to break through, and there were the less visible barriers maintained between the hospital and nearby Lennoxtown which at one stage prevented local people from working there. But this physical separation was only a backdrop for the kind of life which develops in an institution like Lennox Castle. Goffman argues that separation from the world outside enforced by bizarre rules, secrecy, punishments and loss of individual identity, isolated inmates and staff from accepted standards of rationality and ethics in the world 'outside', leading to what Howard Mitchell describes as an 'impenetrable and cruel' community.

Elsewhere Goffman also mentions solidarity among inmates and the development of communal activities. We didn't hear too much about these from the video. Perhaps the riot might be an example of communal resistance, and presumably the football and other sporting activities generated their own group experience. Although a total institution like Lennox Castle might seem like one community from the outside there were clearly times and occasions when, from the inside, it felt as if it contained several different communities.

Goffman has been criticised for drawing conclusions about institutions from a study of only one hospital and for devising a model which focuses on similarities while not allowing for variations within and between hospitals (Jones and Fowles, 1984, pp. 9–26). But as a sociological model the 'total institution' is only a tool to help us organise and identify key features in any context or set of relationships.

Over the years, practices at Lennox Castle Hospital changed. Mixed villas became a feature of life in the 1980s, a far cry from the strict segregation of Colin Sproul and James Lappin's early years at the hospital. Facilities later included a café and shopping area. Sports continued to play a big part in hospital life for both patients and staff. The hospital film shows and dances continued as television was introduced to the villas. Other changes came with the ending of domestic work for patients, to be replaced by education and training, preparation for life outside the hospital. Some element of privacy and individualisation was introduced as cubicles broke up the long rows of hospital beds in the villas and people were allowed to wear their own clothes.

Regulations
regarding the
Visiting of Patients.

1. Patients may be visited on Wednesdays and Saturdays and public holidays, from two till five o'clock, by not more than two friends at a time. In cases of serious illness special permission to visit may be given. On their first visit relatives should see one of the doctors to give information regarding the patient.

2. In conversing with patients visitors should be cheerful, and should not refer to anything that might cause the patient to be discontented.

3. Knives, scissors, needles, and all instruments with which personal injury could be done, are not to be given to patients, neither must letters from patients be taken by visitors to be posted.

4. Visitors are positively prohibited from bringing matches, wine, beer, or spirits into the Institution, or giving same to patients; but visitors may bring or send to their friends fruit, sweets, or cakes, and also newspapers and books. Such should, however, be given to the nurse or attendant, who will afterwards give them to the patient. Permission to give any other article than those mentioned must be obtained from the doctor.

5. Under no circumstances are visitors permitted to give money to patients, or gratuities to nurses or attendants.

6. The special consent of the Superintendent shall be required in the case of visits to patients by persons in connection with business transactions.

7. These regulations are framed in the best interests of the patients, whose welfare is the sole object of the Institution, and infringement of these rules will lead to permission to visit being afterwards refused.

Notice dating from the 1950s

Despite these changes the hospital remains isolated physically and with a distinctive layout determining a way of life and set of care practices which might be seen as normal to the people who live and work there, but far from normal as far as life outside is concerned. Goffman made his observations while he was 'assistant to the athletic director' at one hospital (Jones and Fowles, 1984, p. 23). He had no nursing or administrative experience of hospital life so perhaps he remained very much an outsider while he made his observations. Howard Mitchell tried to combine having been a nurse at Lennox Castle with being a researcher. How did this background contribute to his investigations?

2.3 On being an insider and a researcher

The two roles of practitioner and researcher are not always easy to combine. Sometimes it's difficult to detach yourself from situations and stand back when you know you've been a part of practice which you've begun to see differently. On the other hand, being an insider can bring some advantages. How did Howard Mitchell deal with these two roles?

Activity 5

Weighing up the advantages and disadvantages of being an insider

Allow about 20 minutes

Read through Howard Mitchell's chapter in the Reader (Chapter 2) and as you do, note the advantages and disadvantages that he writes about. How far do you feel he succeeded? Is the video a balanced account or does it feel biased to you in any way? Perhaps it wasn't biased enough for you?

Comment

Advantages: Howard Mitchell mentions his commitment to the hospital, his knowledge of learning disabilities and its history, his contacts with people who could tell him their stories, his local and hospital connections, professional trust, his ability to communicate with people with learning difficulties.

Disadvantages: he was concerned not to upset people who trusted him; he may not have asked enough questions and people assumed he knew things; patients may have deferred to him.

As to bias, Howard explains how he tried not to take on too much medical knowledge of the residents. He deliberately chose not to read their case notes: 'I felt it would be going behind their backs'. The result is that we know nothing about why Margaret and James came to be diagnosed as needing to be detained at Lennox Castle beyond what they told us themselves. But, if people with learning difficulties are to be treated on the same terms as other people in society, then perhaps this is all that we as outsiders should know.

Of course one difference for Howard Mitchell is that he was researching the past. Had he been researching Lennox Castle today he might have found it more difficult to stand back and not intervene or comment on what he heard.

Key points

- Whatever emotions are evoked by the stories we heard in the video, we still need to be able to understand what we saw.

- Using Goffman's model of 'the total institution' is one way to organise and explain what is observed and recorded.

- Models themselves are only a tool to be used critically to identify variations as well as what fits.

- The ways of life which were described provide a starting point for discussions of what are acceptable and normal ways of behaving towards other people.

- Being an insider researcher can have advantages but there are issues of confidentiality and a need to be able to reflect on your part in what you are researching.

Institutions such as Lennox Castle Hospital were typical of a particular period in the history of social care. How did these institutions emerge and what can we learn from that history today? To find out we're going to go back even further into the past.

Section 3
Institutions: an outline history

In this section I'll be compressing most of the history of legislation and provision which came to form the basis of health and social care over the last two centuries into quite a small space! You may want to find out more about particular aspects and developments. If you do, then you'll find the list of references to books and articles at the end of the unit useful. To help you fit things together into a chronology we've constructed a wallchart of the most relevant changes since 1900. It might be useful to keep it by you as you read through this section.

3.1 Institutions and segregation

At one time, poverty, madness, disability and criminality were thought of as unchangeable God-given or demonic states. In the late eighteenth and early nineteenth centuries institutional care emerged as these conditions came to be viewed as treatable. Because it was believed that people could be improved in some way by being set apart from influences which were seen as damaging (like poor families, disease and lack of education) prisons, hospitals and asylums were designed with highly regimented and controlling regimes. Indeed earlier provision for adults and children with learning difficulties focused specifically on education and training programmes. An ethic of work was fundamental to many of these systems of care – work was seen as improving and at the same time providing for inmates' and patients' keep. Institutions also had the function of protecting other people whom, it was thought, might be at risk from contact with poor, mad, disabled or law-breaking members of society.

Previously, people with mental illness had been subjected to degrading practices, often being treated as public spectacles to be ridiculed and terrorised. Many of the nineteenth century reformers wanted to offer more humane treatment yet at the same time they were keen to provide opportunities for the medical profession to experiment with and treat more cases. Charles Dickens, writing in 1841, portrays Barnaby Rudge as someone with learning difficulties. His words are uncritical, but at the same time serve to distance his readers from his main character's humanity. They illustrate the dilemma he faced in writing about such a subject at that time:

> Startling as his aspect was, the features were good, and there was something even plaintive in his wan and haggard aspect. But the absence of a soul is far more terrible in a living man than a dead one, and in this unfortunate being its noblest powers were wanting.

> (Dickens, 1841, p. 28)

Reformers like Lord Shaftesbury supported those doctors who believed in removing chains and adopting a more caring regime, such as that developed at the Retreat in York which had been opened by Quakers as early as 1796. However while Shaftesbury was arguing for a more enlightened philosophy of care he also referred to 'patients', 'hospitals' and 'doctors'. A new language designating conditions which had been thought of in 'moral' terms emerged as people came to be classified as 'insane', 'imbeciles' and 'idiots' which at the time were seen as scientific terms. With the new language came new courses of treatment, including bathing, mild sedative drugs, poultices and enemas. One system and

Bethlehem Hospital, London, women's gallery, 1860

language of care was thus substituted by another, more medical one (Nolan, 1993, pp. 33–5). In Unit 1 we looked at the way words used to describe different conditions and disabilities change, with each change marking shifts in attitudes and in care practice.

The 1845 Lunacy Act and the Lunacy (Scotland) Act of 1857 required the counties or local authorities to build and maintain asylums. These new environments were seen as providing the basis for reforming difficult behaviours or treating illnesses. They provided a total environment of treatment, support and work for their inmates. The institutions, the treatment regimes and the segregation, it was believed, would contribute to some kind of cure. And of course, because they were so segregated, the general public had little opportunity to witness what went on within. This encouraged a belief that they were curative or at least therapeutic in some way.

The Retreat near York, from an early 19th century engraving

Within the asylums, doctors' powers tended to be unquestioned and were supported by public fears whipped up by contemporary newspaper reports. Indeed, in England and Wales the number of people certified as 'lunatics' doubled between 1844 and 1860, leading some people at the time to question the reliability of such assessments. Were publicity and social panic having an effect on judgments (Nolan, 1993, p. 33)? The growth in the numbers also had its effect on the operation of care within the institution as 'cure and treatment' could easily become 'control and punishment'.

A distinctive feature of the asylums was their size. We began the unit with a look at how remarkable many of these buildings were in terms of architecture and layout. While the first asylums, like the Retreat at York, were meant for only 30 patients, by 1900 buildings came to average over 800. Colney Hatch, the Middlesex asylum which opened in 1851, was from the start designed for 1,000 patients. Its frontage was nearly one-third of a mile long (Alaszewski, 1986, p. 8).

These early institutions developed out of Elizabethan Poor Law provision where those whose families could not care for them or who were unable to provide for themselves were supported out of local parish funds in workhouses and small institutions.

3.2 Social darwinism and eugenics

Nineteenth century reformers combined their new medical diagnoses with a concern to tackle what they saw as the social causes of cruelty and incapacity. Two theories dominated: social darwinism and eugenics.

Social darwinism drew on Darwin's ideas of natural selection and emphasised the contribution of the fittest and most superior individuals to the survival of the human species. The social darwinists, who included some of the most prominent thinkers of their time, believed that social 'engineering' or the control or manipulation and improvement of social conditions would do away with, or weaken, the effect of nature's shaping forces. The result would be uncontrolled breeding and weakening of the genetic pool and hence the deterioration of the race and swamping of the higher types within society. Eugenicists took these ideas further, arguing that those who were weaker, 'degenerate' or 'defective' in some way should not be allowed to breed or interbreed at all as their offspring would inevitably degrade the quality of the race. Poverty, ignorance, mental defectiveness as well as lack of moral values were seen as evidence that British society needed to purify its genetic stock and deal with what were seen as poisonous environments in the slums and factories. Great emphasis was placed on parenthood and procreation.

Child with learning disability from the nineteenth century, MENCAP archive

The influence of the eugenics movement in this country was strong and had a particularly pernicious effect on the care of children with learning difficulties. Ideas based on notions of racial purity led to demands for compulsory sterilisation of young people with learning difficulties and the application of a condemnatory morality which saw unmarried mothers locked away in mental handicap institutions. Their custodial care came largely to be accepted by the medical and educational establishments and their situation largely invisible to wider society (Hendrick, 1994, p. 92).

These ideas sustained segregation as a form of provision of care: segregation from society and segregation of the sexes within institutions (Williams, 1989, pp. 160–1).

Eugenicist ideas flourished well into the twentieth century and, some argue, are still alive today, with concern about reproduction a persistent thread as these quotes and the cuttings overleaf demonstrate:

The unnatural and increasingly rapid growth of the feeble-minded classes, coupled with a steady restriction among all the thrifty, energetic and superior stocks constitutes a race danger. I feel that the source from which the stream of madness is fed should be cut off and sealed up before another year has passed.

(Churchill, a proponent of forcible sterilisation, in a private letter to Prime Minister Asquith at the time of the Royal Commission on the Care and Control of the Feeble-Minded, 1904, quoted in Ponting, 1992, p. 23)

[It is] not the very severe cases which are the most dangerous: it is the mild cases, which are capable of being well veneered, so as to look, for a time at any rate, almost normal, against which there is most need to protect society.

(Mary Dendy, proponent of segregation, writing in 1910, quoted in Jackson, 1996, p. 166)

While *dementia* means being 'out of one's mind' *amentia* was used as another word for 'mental deficiency' or a lack of mind.

Let us assume that we could segregate as a separate community all the families in the country containing mental defectives of the primary amentia type. We should find that we had collected among them a most interesting social group. It would include everyone who has extensive practical experience of social service would readily admit, a much larger proportion of insane persons, epileptics, paupers, criminals (especially recidivists), unemployables, habitual slum dwellers, prostitutes, inebriates and other social inefficients than would a group of families not containing mental defectives. The overwhelming majority of the families thus collected will belong to a section of the community which we propose to term the 'social problem' or 'subnormal group' ... If we are to prevent the racial disaster of mental deficiency we must deal not only with the mentally defective persons but with the whole subnormal group from which the majority of them come ... The relative fertility of this (subnormal) group is greater than that of normal persons.

(Report of the Wood Committee on Mental Deficiency, 1929, quoted in Ryan and Thomas, 1987, p. 108)

3.3 Treatment regimes

As well as asylums which housed people with mental illness and learning difficulties there was a turn towards a style of mass provision generally.

Development of special schools for disabled children began in 1750 when the first private schools for blind and deaf children were opened in Britain. The earliest public institution, run on a charitable basis, the London Asylum for the 'support and education of the deaf and dumb children of the poor', was opened in Bermondsey, south London, in 1792. By the end of the nineteenth century, separate schools for blind, deaf, physically disabled and learning disabled children were common, though the extent to which they were educational rather than custodial was much debated. Poor Law children were similarly treated to segregated and reforming regimes. They might be fostered or 'boarded out' but were just as likely to be housed in district schools, 'barrack schools' or to be placed in voluntary society homes run by organisations such as Dr Barnardo's and the National Children's Home (Hendrick, 1994, pp. 76–8). Barnardo spoke for many reformers when he argued

A woman's right to a screen test

In Guardian Health (Nov 16), Brian Wilson MP accuses those involved in the development of antenatal screening programmes for Down's syndrome of exploitation. We are said to promote fear by an emphasis on handicap, to have financial motivation, and to be preoccupied with abortion, all of which, he claims, devalues disabled people.

(Guardian, 7 December 1993)

The genetic tyranny

(Independent on Sunday, 18 July 1993)

Master race of the Left

Forced sterilisations in Scandinavia have shocked the world. But the great founding fathers of British socialism had dreams almost as vile as those of the Nazis.

(Guardian, 30 August 1997)

Protest to Vatican after disabled are urged to avoid sex

Italian organisations for the handicapped yesterday protested to the Vatican over assertions that physically and mentally disabled people should abstain from sex to ensure they did not 'infect' their partners or produce handicapped children.

(The Times, 2 July 1997)

Sweden regrets its eugenic past

Sweden is re-examining its progressive image after the revelation that 60,000 of its citizens were sterilised on dubious grounds.

Some have compared the sterilisations to the brutal treatment of Nazi Germany, which also tried to rid itself of those it considered inferior.

(Guardian, 26 August 1997)

Gene study rejects compulsory testing for life insurance

The British are more likely to die from cancer and heart disease than people from 26 of the world's most developed nations. Both illnesses can be passed on in genes, but compulsory genetic testing for those applying for life insurance is too expensive and too complicated to be worthwhile, according to a survey published today.

(The Times, 17 June 1997)

Dumbie House where Thomas Braidwood established the first school for deaf children, 'Braidwood's Academy for The Deaf and Dumb' in 1760. Photograph taken in 1935

that if the children of the poor, whether or not they had parents, 'can be removed from their surroundings early enough, and can be kept sufficiently long under training, heredity counts for little, environment counts for everything' (quoted in Hendrick, 1994, p. 79). Today we might see these attitudes as rooted in the nineteenth century ethic of work and individual self-improvement.

It has been argued that institutional care increasingly came to be used by working class families who, under pressure from the effects of long working hours for most members of the family and urban overcrowding, found it less possible to care for people at home than in earlier, pre-industrial times and that factory work provided fewer opportunities for people with learning difficulties. As home and work became more separate, so care and support became less possible

Warren Towers School for the Deaf, Newmarket, 1939

(Ignatieff, 1983). Wright argues that if family members were given over to asylum care this was not necessarily because parents and others had a medicalised understanding. Lay explanations of learning disability were more likely to be linked to growing children's inability to contribute to the household economy and especially to their apparent inability to benefit from education (Wright, 1996, p. 131). This theory fits well with James Lappin's explanation of why his father handed him over to hospital care.

While Wright's suggestion is an interesting one it needs to be born in mind that care in the community and by families continued to be the dominant form of care throughout the period when institutions flourished. Many parents resisted pressure to put their children into institutions, as Ida Taylor, born in 1921 with cerebral palsy recalls:

> *They wanted to send me to a mental place and lock me up. They kept coming to our house when I was about six or seven years old to ask me and my mum questions. They asked me easy things like me name and how many days in the week and about money and that. Me and me mum got upset because I didn't want to go away and she didn't want them to take me. They said I should be in a mental place and that worried us a lot. What stopped it was that me mum took me to our doctor. He stopped those men coming round and told them I was no more mental than fly! They'd been on at us for about five years and it had made me mum ill with worry thinking I was going to be locked up.*
>
> (Quoted in Humphries and Gordon, 1992, p. 16)

Arguments that institutional solutions suited a society in which working class families had fewer resources to support their disabled relatives does not explain why institutional solutions were also taken up by wealthier middle and upper-class families who resorted to the private asylums. Though the treatment of poor children in the workhouse was satirised by Charles Dickens in his novel *Oliver Twist* there was no parallel popular exposure of the treatment of those who were considered 'insane' or 'imbeciles'. Those, both staff and patients, who protested about conditions in the nineteenth century asylums, like John Perceval and his Alleged Lunatics' Friend Association which was founded with the backing and help of lawyers, were isolated. They lacked the powers of resistance to what had come to be seen as a normal and acceptable way to treat certain groups of people judged to be in need of care and protection.

We've mentioned the impact of the 1845 and 1857 (Scotland) Lunacy Acts. These Acts made no distinction between people with a mental illness and people with learning difficulties. Separate provision for people with learning difficulties only came later with the 1913 Mental Deficiency Act, as we heard on the video. Until then only a tiny minority of people certified as 'idiots' lived in specialist 'idiot asylums'; the rest lived in workhouses, prisons and lunatic asylums (Gladstone, 1996, p. 140).

The proportion of people living in mental hospitals peaked in the 1930s and began to decline in the 1950s. In contrast, the peak for numbers of people with learning difficulties in institutions came in the 1960s *after* the 1959 Mental Health Act which gave more emphasis to community care. Their numbers actually trebled between 1924 and 1954 to reach nearly 60,000 (Alaszewski, 1986, p. 15). The influence of institutional care persisted long and powerfully, as we've seen from the history of Lennox Castle Hospital.

Activity 6   **What about segregation today?**

Allow about 5 minutes   Just pause for a moment and think about who gets segregated in society today, where, and why. Write down any groups of people you can think of.

Comment   I thought of people convicted of criminal behaviour serving prison sentences, some people with learning difficulties, disabled children at special schools, young offenders, asylum seekers, illegal immigrants, people who are unable to pay their debts or who have been convicted of fraud, children in care or boarding schools, homeless people in night shelters and hostels, women who are victims of domestic violence who live in refuges, frail older people in nursing homes and residential care. I also thought of people detained under the Mental Health Act because they are diagnosed by doctors as being a danger to themselves or to others, and people detained under Section 47 of the 1948 National Assistance Act because they are neglecting themselves.

These days they may not be so great in number and the buildings they live in may be less imposing, but have all the reasons for segregation changed so very much?

Court denies brain damage boy his choice of school

A couple yesterday lost what could be the final round of their three-year fight to send their brain-damaged son to a mainstream comprehensive rather than a school for children with special needs.

(*Guardian*, 13 May 1997)

Project Worker – Intake Hospital

£18,162 Kings Cros

Providing a safe and supportive envir
homeless men and women aged 16–
moving into independent housing will
In addition to the practical managem
during your shift, you will be respons
and interviewing new residents, provi
on topics ranging from basic life ski
opportunities and liaising with referr
organisations and statutory bodies.

At least a year's experience of sup
from black and ethnic minority grou
a keywork system will therefore be
good understanding of legislation a
young homeless people. Capable
situations, supervising volunteers
workload, you will also need to d
interpersonal and report writing
undertake weekend work and sl

If you share our commitment to
young people and would like fu
an A4 size 39p SAE to Sandra R
House, 2 Swallow Place, Londo
with the relevant reference. Cl

WORKING TOWARDS E

Harp's Oak Children's Ho

Where Quality Care Counts
Registered with Surrey County Council

A quality residential home catering for young people with em
difficulties and/or exhibiting challenging behaviour, both
female aged 13–17.

We offer:
- Long, short & medium term care.
- Emergency referrals welcome.
- Education on site.
- Individual care packages & plans.
- Assessment of need.
- Creative activity programme.
- Experienced & skilled staff team.
- Structural approach.

As we have now been established for two years and operate
regime, from which we measure our success. We would lik
you the opportunity to share this success with us, therefore ar
an introductory discount to all new placements for the first
a young persons stay with us.

Further enquiries please contact Mike Walker

Principal manager at:

Harp's Oak Children's Home
180 London Road North, Merstham,
Redhill, Surrey RH1 3BP.

Can you work with homeless offenders in Haringey or Barnet?
Two Housing Resettlement Posts

Haringey Barnet Team (Ref: WHB/2/97)
Starting Salary: £16,587 p.a. inc LW
(1997 Pay award pending)

We have a vacancy in this five-person team, which manages four houses for twenty six offenders in Haringey and Barnet. The aim of the Offender Projects is to help residents lead a life free from crime and harmful dependency. We do this by providing individual support and a resettlement service which is intended to increase residents' life and social skills.
You will need at least twelve months experience of support/social skills work, group and one-to-one work and have the ability and enthusiasm to contribute to a structured resettlement programme which is attractive to residents.
You should have the skills to enable you to respond positively and creatively to the needs of people who have been involved in a wide range of offending behaviour, be a good communicator, be committed to providing services within an Equal Opportunities framework, have experience of administrative work and knowledge of the benefits system.
Terms: In addition to the salary, which is based on NJC Scale 6–SO1 points 26–31, NWLHA offers a benefits package which includes 30 days holiday per annum and non-contributory pension scheme.

Application form and recruitment pack from: NWLHA, 3rd Floor, 293–299 Kentish Town Road, London NW5 2TJ or telephone during office hours only. Completed application forms should be received no later than 21 July 1997 quoting the above reference number. Interview date is 28 July 1997.

NWLHA is striving to be an Equal Opportunities Employer but regrets its premises are not presently wheelchair accessible. All NWLHA offices are non-smoking.

So far we've discussed asylums and large-scale institutions simply in terms of the policies which gave rise to them and the philosophies which supported them, both inside and out. But these institutions were also places of employment. How did the job of nursing develop under such conditions?

Key points

- The nineteenth century saw the development of large-scale institutions designed to segregate, control and in some cases, cure, their inmates.

- The philosophy of institutional care meant that people from most sections of society tended to be catered for, from the youngest to the oldest, although care at home in the community was still the most likely form of care.

- Social darwinism and eugenics were influential philosophies which, together with an increase in the power of the medical professions, led to policies which segregated particular groups from society and which also imposed sexual segregation within institutions to prevent interbreeding.

- Policies of segregation still operate today and affect certain individuals and groups within society.

3.4 The emergence of asylum professionals

Asylums and institutions were not only sites of care and control, they were also places where people worked as staff and developed professional expertise. The people who worked there also experienced segregation, professionally speaking. In this section we take a brief look at the development of caring professions in the institutions.

Low status patients, frequently paupers, with low status illnesses and conditions, such as mental illness, mental frailty or mental handicap, provided no prestige to doctors and other staff who worked with them. These socially stigmatising conditions meant that asylum doctors in mid-nineteenth century England occupied a lower social and professional status than doctors who worked in general hospitals. They could not, for example, offer their services to the large public charities or other bodies. They could not become consultants. Assistant medical officers in the asylums were paid at a lower rate, had to live in, had to delay marriage and had few opportunities for research or professional development. Since doctors at the large general and teaching hospitals did not see people with mental illness, there was also a tendency towards segregation of knowledge and professional skills (Hurt, 1988, p. 115).

If the medical staff were regarded as low in status, the attendants, as asylum nurses were still being called until well after the Second World War, who looked after the patients were very much lower, both within the institutions and within nursing generally. Though the Medico-Psychological Association (MPA), the asylum doctors' own organisation, was ostensibly in support of training and education for attendants, with several members running their own evening classes during the mid to late nineteenth century, there was concern that successful nurses might challenge the position of doctors. However, by 1899 over a hundred asylums were taking part in a training scheme which led to an examination and certification. Attendants who took part were almost exclusively from the public asylums and were supervised and trained by doctors. This was in contrast with general nurses who, led by such pioneers as Florence Nightingale, had set up training schools which were controlled by nurses. Few private institutions trained their own attendants. Nursing had its own professional organisation by 1887 with the establishment of the British Nursing Association. But asylum nurses were excluded from membership on the grounds that they did not have appropriate experience and were also socially inferior.

In the box below are the examination questions for attendants sitting the MPA's Diploma in 1893. Candidates were charged 2s 6d (approximately one tenth of an average weekly wage) and resits cost one shilling. Remember that at this stage, before the 1913 Mental Deficiency Act, asylums included many people with learning difficulties as well as those who were regarded as mentally ill.

Examination for attendants on the insane (1893)

1   Mention the causes of lung disease.

2   By what channels is the refuse or waste matter of the body drained from the circulation?

3   What symptoms would lead you to suspect that a patient is losing weight?

4   What symptoms would lead you to suspect that a patient is gaining weight?

5   (a)   What is a sensory nerve?

    (b)   What is a motor nerve?

6   Name the special senses.

7   (a)   What is a drawsheet?

    (b)   Explain how you would use it.

    (c)   What are its advantages?

8   (a)   What observations would you make regarding the passage of urine and

    (b)   the appearance of the urine?

9   (a)   Why is occupation important in the treatment of the insane?

    (b)   What rules should be observed in promoting the occupation of patients?

10   (a)   What patients are most likely to escape?

    (b)   What circumstances would make you suspicious?

    (c)   How would you guard against escape?

11   (a)   In what way should attendants conduct themselves towards patients?

    (b)   What do you understand by 'showing a good example'?

12   (a)   What are the risks in treating cases in private houses compared with asylums?

    (b)   What precautions would you take?

13   What are the difficulties with relatives in private houses, and how would you endeavour to meet them?

(Quoted in Nolan, 1993, p. 67)

Activity 7   Skills for the attendants

Allow about 5 minutes   Look at the exam questions in the box. What does it seem that the attendants' main tasks might have been and what key skills did they need?

Comment   The first part of the paper, up to question 4, focuses on physical health or changes in the condition of patients. Then questions 5 and 6 might possibly be described as rudimentary psychology. These are followed by a question which seems to be more about control and security. There doesn't seem to be much about communication, or emotional or spiritual care, and there's only question 9 to suggest that the attendants or nurses might also need to know how to divert or stimulate patients mentally.

Question 13 is interesting for what it reveals about contact with patients' relatives. It seems to suggest that only staff working in the community were likely to have to explain themselves to patients' families about the treatment being provided.

The tasks might be summarised as: diagnosis, treatment, containment and protection.

As to study skills, this paper seems quite demanding in terms of the verbal and writing skills it expects in such a low status occupation. Just for your information it's perhaps worth adding that the written paper was followed by a practical part, held two or three days later. Both parts of the exam were marked by the attendants' own superintendent and an external assessor who was also an asylum superintendent.

In 1920 the newly formed General Nursing Council agreed that those who held the MPA's Certificate and those who had gained the newly established Certificate for Nurses in Mental Subnormality, could be eligible to be admitted to the supplementary Register (Nolan, 1993, pp. 60–81). When Colin Sproul became an attendant at Lennox Castle he and his colleagues took the Royal Medico-Psychological Association examination to obtain a certificate in 'mental deficiency nursing'. This was a lesser qualification, with State Registered Nurses (SRNs) occupying higher status.

Colin Sproul was to become a shop steward later in his career. Trade unionism among the asylum nurses made a number of attempts to get off the ground in the nineteenth century as attendants tried to break free from the discipline and harshness of the medical hierarchy running the asylums. The basis for successful organisation came with the National Asylum Workers' Union, set up in 1910. This was to change its name in 1931 to the Mental Hospitals and Institutional Workers' Union amalgamating with the Hospitals and Welfare Services Union in 1946 to form the Confederation of Health Service Employees (COHSE). In 1993 COHSE joined with two other public service unions, NUPE and NALGO, to form the giant union UNISON.

Institutions varied and it would be inaccurate to portray them all, and all their staff, as insensitive custodians. However this particular form of provision had some dominant characteristics which meant that, as far as the general public was concerned, it was something to be avoided. Why were institutions perceived in this way?

We've looked at Goffman's characteristics of life in institutions and we've seen that, although they were never the main form of care, institutions dominated the landscape and language of care provision. What was the nature of their domination and what did it mean for the reputation which they had in society generally?

The Royal Medico-Psychological Association.

This is to Certify that

COLIN CAMPBELL SPROULL

having been duly trained at

LENNOX CASTLE INSTITUTION

according to the Regulations of the Association has shown in examination Proficiency in the Nursing of Mental Defectives including Section "A"

Signed _John R Bath Robbem_ Medical Examiner.

Countersigned a. Helen Boyle — President.

H P L Haynes. Registrar.

Dated December, 1939.

Nº 3062

SECTION A —	BEDSIDE NURSING.	
„ B —	SPECIAL METHOD OF TEACHING MENTALLY DEFECTIVE CHILDREN.	
„ C —	THE TRAINING OF MENTALLY DEFECTIVE ADULTS.	
„ D —	PHYSICAL TRAINING, DRILL, DANCING, INDOOR AND OUTDOOR AMUSEMENTS.	

Colin Sproul's nursing certificate, 1939

Activity 8   **Resistance to institutions**

Allow about 30 minutes

Turn to Chapter 7 in the Reader. Read it through and note down an example for each of what Parker suggests are the 'four forms of reinforcement' of attitudes towards institutional care during the nineteenth and twentieth centuries. Think back to the video. Does what you saw support Parker's argument?

Comment   Parker's 'four forms of reinforcement' are:

1   'The deliberate cultivation of a repellent image': he suggests that this followed from the implementation of the poor law and its philosophy of deterrence and oppression which permeated institutional provision from the start.

2   'Reported cases of abuse of inmates': he mentions scandals as well as routine cruelties.

3   'Enforced association and routine of institutional life': he quotes Townsend (1962) and a warehousing approach to care which forced people to live in an 'artificial' community in which they lost their own individuality.

4   'Compulsion': he mentions the practice of certification and lack of understanding of the differences between mental handicap and mental illness. Certification under the Mental Deficiency Act of 1913 placed on local authorities the responsibility to ensure that all adults and children considered 'mentally defective' should be identified by a specially appointed Executive Officer and examined and certified by a doctor. A patient's certification was reviewed every five years before a committee, but was rarely revoked.

How did you see these 'four forms of reinforcement' in relation to Lennox Castle? Was its image 'repellent'? Margaret Scally and James Lappin seemed to have mixed feelings about the place. As an ex-inmate perhaps Margaret is more forthright in her critical expressions. Howard Mitchell describes its dubious reputation within the wider community but seems to see both positive and negative sides to its past.

What about abuse and scandals? Well we did hear about behaviour which by today's standards might be regarded as unsatisfactory and unacceptable in relation to patients.

'Enforced association' sounds like Goffman's description of the total institution. Margaret, Colin and James's accounts are full of references to people being regimented in groups and having opportunities for individuality suppressed.

Compulsion and detention was certainly a feature of Lennox Castle's care regime. We heard about the young men who were detained there as an alternative to prison and it certainly seemed as if James and Margaret had not had much choice until recently about where they might live, despite the ending of certification in 1959.

Parker was writing at a time (1988) when all forms of institutional care, including residential care, were under review. His hope, expressed at the end of the chapter, is that, given time, memories of past abuses would fade and that a new, more positive view of collective forms of provision might emerge coupled with more enlightened and sympathetic practice.

> **Key points**
>
> - Institutional care tended to be provided for those who had a low status in society, either from poverty or disability.
> - The staff also occupied a low status within the hierarchy of their professions.
> - Low status, 'repellent image', association with the poor law and a philosophy of deterrence and oppression meant that as far as the general public was concerned institutional care was regarded with fear and horror.

3.5 Campaigns for change

In Unit 3, the section 'Forces for change' outlined the political and economic changes as well as the shifts in opinion which led to the move towards community care in the mid-twentieth century. Here we consider where some of the pressure for change was coming from in the earlier part of the twentieth century. Throughout the period of institutional domination there were, as we've seen from the early 1800s, voices which called out for change. Some contrasted the treatment of the sick and disabled poor with their richer counterparts in the private asylums. Others protested at the general inhumanity of regimented, mass care. Patients and their relatives had mixed experiences to draw on, but few felt confident enough to speak out in public against abuse or to suggest alternative forms of care. Shame was also a powerful deterrent to speaking out. Relatives were often unwilling to admit that a relative was an inmate of an institution. When change came it was as a result of action taken by people who were, for a variety of reasons, more powerfully situated. One source was the increasing professionalisation of those involved in the care of poorer and more dependent people in society.

Professionalisation

Care of frail older people provides an example. Many were cared for in the old Poor Law Infirmaries which had become the responsibility of local authorities by the early decades of the twentieth century. These tended to be considered, by patients, doctors and nurses alike, as very much second class to voluntary aided hospitals (Timmins, 1996, p. 106). Nevertheless, even within the voluntary hospitals older people often fared least well, living for years on 'back wards' allocated for the 'chronic sick'. Many of these wards existed well into the 1950s and became the subject of exposures and critical comment, particularly following the efforts of Dr Marjorie Warren who campaigned among the medical profession for the recognition of geriatric medicine as a speciality. She wrote in 1946:

> It is surprising that the medical profession has been so long in awakening to its responsibilities towards the chronic sick and the aged, and that the country at large should have been content to do so little for this section of the community. Today, owing to the ageing of the population, the general shortage of nurses and domestic help ... and the fact that more women are employed ... the problem has reached enormous dimensions ... To all who have studied the subject it is obvious that the specialised care and treatment of these folk is of great economic importance and calls for immediate attention.
>
> (Quoted in Evers, 1993, p. 320)

Marjorie Warren targeted doctors who she felt neglected older people in the infirmaries because they were poor and suffering from conditions requiring lengthy treatment for which often there was no cure. The first Chair of Geriatric Medicine was set up in the late 1960s in Glasgow, a few years after Marjorie Warren's death (Evers, 1993, p. 323). You'll find an account of the beginning of changing practice in Chapter 1 in the Reader.

Civil Liberties campaigns

Another source of change came from changing attitudes in the area of civil liberties. The Mental Deficiency Act of 1913 had defined categories

Cover of 50,000 Outside the Law, *pamphlet on the treatment of mental health patients, National Council for Civil Liberties, 1951*

50,000
OUTSIDE THE LAW

An examination of the treatment of those certified as mental defectives

of mental deficiency on social grounds with the result that many men, women and children had been locked up for years without any diagnosis relating to mental deficiency. The pressure group, the National Council for Civil Liberties (now known as Liberty) began campaigning in 1947 for a change in the Act. The NCCL's campaign included the identification of 850 'mental deficiency' cases, for example Kathleen Bradley who had been detained for 20 years. At the age of 19, recovering from rheumatic fever, her local authority had been unable to find anyone to look after her. Though she had been in the top class at her school and had no record of being a delinquent she had been certified as a 'mental defective'. A campaign to release her included questions in Parliament and appeals to the Board of Control. She was released in 1955.

The success of the NCCL's campaign and the realisation that there were probably approaching 6,000 similar cases led to the setting up of a Royal Commission in 1957. The Royal Commission was followed fairly swiftly by the 1959 Mental Health Act which abolished the 1913 Act and introduced Mental Health Review Tribunals. These had to include at least one non-professional member. The NCCL led teams of volunteers to act for patients at tribunals and by 1958 1,800 people had been released, with others following later (Dyson, 1994, pp. 33–35). Though the NCCL had identified injustice with some success, certification was replaced by compulsory detention defined in various sections of the 1959 and successive Mental Health Acts, a practice which came to be known as being 'on section' or 'sectioning' which is still in force today. The old Mental Deficiency Act's powers were curbed by the 1959 Act but people previously classified 'feeble minded' were reclassified as 'severely subnormal' and were still compulsorily detained.

Scandals, treatments and cost saving

In the 1960s critics of the quality of care for older people, such as Peter Townsend, *The Last Refuge* (1962), and Barbara Robb, *Sans Everything* (1967), added their voices to growing criticisms of institutional care, not only for older people but for users of mental health services and people with learning difficulties too. Government had already begun to take account of its responsibilities for the dire state and cost of many of these institutions and in a famous speech in 1961 Enoch Powell, the then Minister of Health, spoke in damning terms:

> *There they stand, isolated, majestic, imperious, brooded over by the gigantic water tower and chimney combined, rising unmistakable and daunting out of the countryside – the asylums which our forefathers built with such immense solidity.*

(Quoted in Timmins, 1996, p. 211)

Powell set up a 10-year plan but little was achieved at that stage. Successive governments inherited the scandals and, without a convincing or funded alternative, his words did little more than start a process of change. The campaigns of the 1950s and 1960s led by voluntary organisations, academics and some professionals, as well as by patients and their families, fuelled a general move away from institutional care which was given statutory support in the 1990 NHS and Community Care Act as we saw in Unit 3. There were other changes too. The introduction of drug treatment from the 1950s offered the possibility of non-custodial care and ideas about the origins and development of conditions began to change too. More psychological and psychotherapeutic as opposed to physiological theories took over, and ideas about correcting or treating behaviour began to lose their force (Parker in the Reader, Chapter 7).

Institutions were never the major providers of care in the UK; a range of other types of provision coexisted so that those in institutional care were always a minority of those receiving care. But institutions have tended to be the lynch pin as such terms as 'preventive care', 'after care', 'care after discharge' suggest. All these 'other' forms of provision relate back somewhere to institutional care. As Parker suggests, institutions always dominated the landscape of care provision. The training they provided to nursing and medical staff, their care regimes and their position as a last resort, meant that they constituted a powerful source of authority and control in the lives of people who, for whatever reason, came within their confines.

Activity 9 **Living through change**

Allow about 15 minutes

Colin Sproul and James Lappin were both in their eighties when they were interviewed for the video. Margaret Scally was 44. In the box opposite there's a time line which integrates dates and events in their lives with some of the events mentioned in the wallchart. I've also included some key political events which could be significant. Read it through and, as you do, note down any questions it raises for you about the lives of Colin, James and Margaret.

Colin Sproul, 1997

Colin Sproul (second from left) and colleagues, 1938

Margaret Scally in Glasgow, 1997

Margaret Scally at the Special Olympics

James Lappin at Lennox Castle Hospital, 1997

James Lappin back in Glasgow on a visit

Living through changes

1908 – Royal Commission on the Care and Control of the Feeble-Minded

1910 – James Lappin born

1913 – Mental Deficiency Act (England and Scotland)

1915 – Colin Sproul born

1914–18 – First World War

1925 – James goes into Royal Scottish National Institution at Larbert

1927 – Mental Deficiency Act

1929 – Report of the Mental Deficiency Committee (Wood Committee); recommended expansion of institutional provision for 'mental defectives'

1937 – Colin joins the staff at Lennox Castle Hospital

1938 – James enters Lennox Castle Hospital

1939 – Outbreak of Second World War

1939 – Colin Sproul qualifies as a mental deficiency nurse

1942 – Colin marries and moves onto the Oval shortly afterwards

1945 – Labour government

1946 – National Health Service Act

1947 – National Council for Civil Liberties campaign begins

1951 – Conservative government

1952 – Margaret Scally born

1952 – The drug Chlorpromazine (Largactil) introduced

1956 – Riot at Lennox Castle

1957 – Report of the Royal Commission on the Law Relating to Mental Illness and Deficiency (The Percy Report)

1958 – Margaret is admitted to Waverley Park Home

1959 – Mental Health Act 1961

1961 – Enoch Powell's 'water tower' speech

1962 – Peter Townsend's *Last Refuge* published

1964 – Labour government

1967 – Barbara Robb's *Sans Everything* published

1960s (late) – Employment of patients as domestics on the wards at Lennox Castle ends

1968 – Margaret is moved to Lennox Castle Hospital

1969 – Ely report identifies cruelty and cover-up at the Ely mental hospital in Cardiff; first of a decade of several similar inquiries at Farleigh, Whittingham, South Ockenden and Normansfield

1971 – *Better Services for the Mentally Handicapped*, White Paper issued by the Department of Health

1972 – 'Our Life', first national conference of people with learning difficulties

1975 – Non-contributory Invalidity Pension introduced for all patients, at £3.00 a week

1975 – Colin retires

1979 – Committee of Enquiry into Mental Handicap Nursing and Care (the Jay Committee) stresses the importance of individual care rather than groups or classes of care

1979 – Conservative government

1981 – Association of Carers founded

1986 – Report by the Audit Commission, *Making a Reality of Community Care*

1988 – *Community Care: Agenda for Action* (Griffiths Report) – did not extend officially to Scotland

1988 – *Residential Care: A Positive Choice* (Wagner Report) – did not extend officially to Scotland

1989 – *Caring for People*, White Paper issued by Department of Health – includes Scotland

1990 – National Health Service and Community Care Act (includes Scotland)

1991 – Margaret moves into the community

1997 – James is living at Lennox Castle

1997 – Colin is living in Lennoxtown

1997 – Labour government

Comment   *One of the first questions I wanted to ask is how was it that James Lappin could have spent nearly 37 years, getting on for half of his life, in Lennox Castle since the 1959 Mental Health Act which emphasised community treatment and which led to many people being freed from the label of 'certification'? I wondered how long it took for legislation and the effect of reports to change care practices at Lennox Castle. I wondered whether, had James Lappin only been born a few years earlier, he would have been certified and put into hospital at all. There didn't seem to be much detail to fill in for Colin and Margaret's lives. I wondered whether the time line would have looked different had they had an opportunity on the video to discuss the changes which were important to them, like friends they'd known, different jobs they'd done and family events.*

The time line brings together various bits of information, from making the video, from the wallchart, from books and other publications, and from this unit. You might have wondered about the different types of facts you were presented with. Some were spoken on the video while others were simply dates of events. Did you wonder how these different kinds of evidence compared with one another? In the next section we're going to look at some different sources of evidence about the past.

Key points

- As far as individuals are concerned, key Acts, reports and other innovations may have little immediate impact on the quality of life – institutions can be slow to change.

- Until very recently the policy and practice of institutional life has dominated the lives of people who are seen to need care.

- When change came it was due to a number of influences: cost reduction, professionalisation of the staff, civil liberties campaigns, scandals and exposures, introduction of new drugs and treatments.

Section 4
Different kinds of evidence: different kinds of history?

When Howard Mitchell was carrying out his researches into Lennox Castle Hospital he had access to many different kinds of evidence. Each contributed a different aspect or angle to the main story. How did they fit together? Were they complementary or did they contradict each other in any way?

4.1 Different kinds of evidence

All the different sources of evidence shown in the video tell us something about how accounts are built up about public institutions and how easy, or difficult, it is to get a complete picture.

Activity 10   **Listing the kinds of evidence**

Allow about 20 minutes   Think back to what you saw on the video and make a list of all the kinds of evidence Howard Mitchell was able to use in finding out about the hospital.

Comment   **Types of evidence**

Howard Mitchell looked at a number of different types of evidence. These included:

- **Original documents** from the hospital's archives and from the archives of the Glasgow Health Board. We saw examples of: patients' case notes, a daily report book, reports from the Commissioners on Lunacy, a visitors' book and a misconduct book for male patients. Note that Howard points out that the punishment book was actually given to him by someone who had worked at the hospital. As hospitals close their records are often thrown away or dispersed, a loss to future historians.

- **A book – *The Book of Lennox Castle*.** This included early photographs and a celebratory account of the construction and opening of the hospital. It was published by Glasgow City Council.

- **Newspaper cuttings** – we saw the story of the riot in the microfilm of the *Kirkintilloch Herald*, kept at Kirkintilloch Library.

- **Photographs** – we only actually saw one picture of patients and staff at the football match between the Celtic 'A' team and staff of the hospital in 1936. Howard Mitchell explains that pictures of everyday life were few.

  Howard mentions, and we see a glimpse of, 'curious three-sided photographs', full face and profile, which were included in each patient's case notes. Photographs of this type were used to 'diagnose certain congenital conditions thought to be associated with "mental deficiency"' and because it was thought at one time that there was 'a strong link between physical appearance on the one hand, and intellectual capacity and social ability, on the other' (Jackson, 1997, p. 86).

- **People's own memories** of hospital life – what is known as *oral history evidence*. Howard Mitchell interviewed several people while he was doing his research. We saw three of them in the video: Colin Sproul, James Lappin and Margaret Scally.

How complementary were all these kinds of evidence? One thing you might have noticed is a difference given in the date of the riot. While Howard says on the video that it was 1957, the newspaper cutting dates it as 1956. Perhaps that's one example of why it's useful to have as many sources as possible. In that way some facts can be corroborated.

If Howard Mitchell only had access to the documents in the public library he would have found out very little about the hospital. *The Book of Lennox Castle* is very much a publicity document, produced by Glasgow Corporation and supported by adverts from the companies who contracted to build the villas, lay the roads and install the heating. He would have had the photograph of the football team and a few press cuttings relating to events at the hospital which newspaper reporters were either invited to or gained access to, in the case of scandals and the riot. He would also have been able to read formal reports about the hospital in committee papers from Glasgow Corporation which are likely to have been deposited in the City Archives, though Howard Mitchell doesn't refer to those in the video.

As far as the general public is concerned, little might be known about Lennox Castle Hospital if this is all the evidence that is available.

Add the documents in the hospital's own archives and those at the Glasgow Health Board Archives and the story becomes much more complicated, with almost overwhelming amounts of detail about visits, punishments, drug rounds, patients and daily incidents reported by nurses during each shift. However, as Howard Mitchell points out on the video:

> *As far as the patients are concerned I think the documentary evidence concerning them only illustrates a patient's life who might be a problem in some ways, or whose life is filled with certainly incidents that are recorded. It doesn't tell you very much about the day-to-day life, the day-to-day workings of a patient who doesn't present many problems.*

But if the whole task of looking after patients is based on the assumption that they are a problem then it's hardly surprising that the records present them in that way. It's important to evaluate the purpose of records and to note how accounts are developed and records maintained, and for what purpose.

4.2 Telling the story of the Lennox Castle riot

We've got an opportunity to compare the way different sources, spoken and written, tell the same story with the example of the riot at Lennox Castle. These accounts share strong similarities. This is a very public story with features which will have been told over and over again, and it's likely that the newspaper account was read at the time by staff at the hospital together with the findings of a report on the incidents following an inquiry carried out by the General Board of Control for Scotland, which was responsible for the overseeing of hospitals. This also appeared in the same newspaper a month later. Let's compare the three accounts.

Activity 11   **Comparing accounts**

Allow about 10 minutes   Turn to Offprint 22. There you'll find three accounts of the riot at Lennox
    Castle which was described on the video. These three accounts differ from
one another. Make a note of the differences and why you think they are
different.

Comment   The *Kirkintilloch Herald's* account of the riot makes use of words which
convey an action-packed incident: patients 'barricaded themselves in',
'pelted warders with a hail of missiles', 'stoned' firemen, police 'rushed' to
the hospital and 'thousands of pounds worth of damage was caused'.

Note that the *Herald* refers to 'warders' rather than nurses and the hospital
is described as a 'Mental Hospital' typically confusing learning disability
with mental illness.

Lennox Castle Riot Inquiry

The General Board of Control for Scotland, in
a report on the incidents at Lennox Castle
Institution on January 13 and 14, say: 'The
outbreak was unpredictable. Most of the patients
involved had no previous record of violence and
others had been engaged in useful occupations
in the grounds for considerable periods.'

(*Kirkintilloch Herald*, February 1956)

Trouble at Lennox Castle

Hoses turned on patients

A riot broke out in Lennox Mental Hospital on Saturday afternoon, when
a number of patients barricaded themselves in a pavilion. Firemen were
forced to turn their hoses on patients who pelted warders with a hail of
missiles. Police who rushed from Kilsyth and Stirling found four inches
of water on the floor.

Eight young men made their way to the clothing store, wrecked windows
and furniture and tried to set fire to the building. Firemen attempting to
tackle the blaze were again 'stoned' by the patients. Thousands of pounds
worth of damage was caused.

(*Kirkintilloch Herald*, January 1956)

There's no sense of who wrote the newspaper report and where their
information came from.

The Board of Control's full account is reported in February's *Kirkintilloch
Herald* and reads rather differently. We read that this was an event which
arose out of a 'personal matter' and which, it seems, was well managed by
staff initially, with patients being 'in good spirits' at one point. The wrecking
of the villa isn't really explained apart from the implication that the men
might have been 'excitable' following the move from the hut to the villa and
there's a reference to their 'mental condition' and 'average mental age of
eight'. They had 'no particular grievance'. Staff were praised for their
'wisdom, resource and courage' in implied contrast with the actions of the
rioters. The whole impression is that this was an unprecedented and
abnormal incident caused by factors which are described and explained in
medical rather than social terms.

Colin Sproul's account doesn't really differ too much; he also uses quite
vivid language. He mentions 'a powder keg', 'troublesome' patients and a
struggle involving bin lids for shields and open razors. But listening to the
way he tells the story it seems that there were some tensions around at
the time that neither of the other two accounts refers to. He seems to be

suggesting that the riot was the result of misjudgment on the part of the medical staff. As a nurse he felt he 'knew something would happen'. The way Colin tells the story, and of course we can see and hear *how* he tells the story, the staff sound heroic in their struggle to subdue the rioters. But, he also conveys a sense of admiration for the patients. As in all stories of violence and struggle, heroes are only heroes if their adversaries are also strong and resourceful.

What we learn from Colin Sproul, in contrast with the official and documentary accounts, is that there was a build-up to the events, that there was an attempt to introduce a different philosophy of care in managing this particular group of men, and that solutions to problems of law and order on the streets of Glasgow were being attempted by imprisoning young men in mental handicap hospitals. What the oral evidence offers is both complementary to and subversive of the official and documentary sources.

By looking at these three versions of the same set of events we can see just how stories get to be told differently depending on who does the telling and for what purpose. It's perhaps worth bearing these differences in mind for the next time you read about an incident of abuse or a disturbance in a care setting. But remember, as ever, the people we didn't hear from when it came to telling the story of the riot were the 'rioters' themselves.

4.3 Memories as evidence

If Howard Mitchell had only relied on what he learnt from interviewing people what would he have missed? Even though he spoke to more people than we were able to include on the video he couldn't possibly manage a representative sample of all the people who ever lived or worked at the hospital. Historians are limited to knowing about the lifetimes of people who are available to talk. There will always be an element of bias because of this.

However, as we've seen, oral history evidence can complement, sometimes reinforce what is in the official documents (Thompson, 1988). The written records provide an administrative and medical record of when and why patients were given different injections and pills, but Margaret and James's stories make this sound more like a detailed and almost obsessive control over their whole lives. We recorded more material for the video than we could use and among this was James's description of being made to take laxative:

> *See there are black draft, salts, syrup of senna, you could pick what you wanted you know. I took the syrup of senna mostly. I always took the syrup of senna mostly, that's sweet stuff. The taste and castor oil too. I didn't like castor oil.*

> What happened if you didn't want to take it?

> *They took you into the kitchen and stand with you until you took it, you know. Just a pain, that syrup of senna pain, you know. And you'd be ready for the toilet, you know.*

Oral history also provides evidence of a more humane side to life at Lennox Castle. For example, Colin Sproul spoke about how nurses and patients together managed the routines set them by the hospital. When Howard Mitchell asked him if he would have changed anything on the wards where he worked, he replied:

*Well I think I would have given them more freedom, you know. I mean
they were mental defectives. I mean the way they were looked after and
treated you'd think they were convicts nearly, you know. I felt sorry for
most of them, you know, specially the kind of low grades. I mean it's
amazing how the high grade patients looked after the low grades, and
dressed them and fed them and everything else, you know ... and yet I
mean they could do that one day, next day they would fight with them,
you know that, they were good with them the low grades who couldn't do
much for themselves.*

Was that a feature of most wards?

Yes. Staff could never have done it. Could never have fed them all.

His account gives a very different impression of ward routines and
patient initiative than might be available from the daily report books
written up on the wards. Oral evidence, the stories people tell about
their experience, can do more than simply complement or corroborate
official sources, it can challenge and subvert assumptions too.

At an individual level the challenge may take the form of self-advocacy
and here oral history has come to be recognised as playing a significant
role. Approaches to the history of learning disability have been affected
by developments in ways of working with people with learning
difficulties which now place emphasis on the importance of *listening to
accounts or experiences of care*. Self advocacy groups started in the 1980s,
organisations such as People First as well as groups and committees in
local day and residential services, supported people with learning
difficulties to speak for themselves. As Dorothy Atkinson suggests, the
turn to self-advocacy has had an effect on the history of learning
disability:

> *The developments in self-advocacy ... have shown that people with
> learning disabilities have the capacity to express themselves, and make
> sense of their lives, providing we are prepared to listen. The use of life
> stories, or biographies, gives us the potential to look at life through the
> eyes of people who have been labelled, and to see their world as they see
> and experience it. The individual story, and the collections of various life
> stories, can begin to challenge the many myths which surround people
> with learning disabilities.*

(Atkinson, 1997, p. 11)

You might like to recall how definite Margaret Scally was about her own
experiences of Lennox Castle and, as an interviewee recorded for the
history of Meanwood Park Hospital in Leeds put it:

> *I'd just like people to know so they can realise what it was we had to go
> through! It's not true what was written down! They did it just to keep us
> locked up, so that people would think we're mental!*

(Fido and Potts, 1989, p. 34)

> **Key points**
>
> • Finding out about a particular aspect of the past means looking for as many different sources as possible since none can present a complete picture and together they provide a more complete story.
>
> • The way accounts are presented will depend on who tells the story and with what purpose.
>
> • Memories of the past help us to access accounts and experiences which don't appear in the formal records.
>
> • Encouraging people with learning difficulties to talk about the past is seen by many people as a way to support self-advocacy and challenge stereotypes about learning disability.

Activity 12   **Anthology chapter**

Allow about 45 minutes

Chapter 1 in the Reader is made up of extracts from the writing of people who have lived and worked in a number of different types of institution. You have already been asked to look at this chapter in Unit 8. Pause and read it right through now, thinking about some of the issues we've been discussing in this unit about institutional life.

Ernest 'Tom' Atkins at Brookfield Orthopaedic Hospital, 1930s

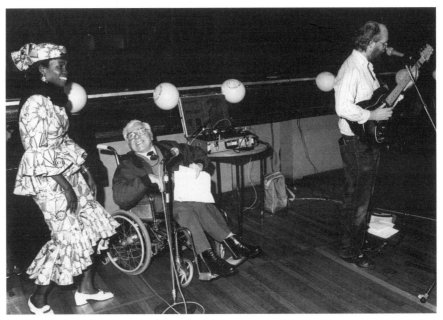

Ernest 'Tom' Atkins at Disability Pride Week, 1992, Waltham Forest, London

An excerpt from Ernest 'Tom' Atkins's story is in Chapter 1 of the Reader.

Comment   You may want to come back to Chapter 1 from time to time as you work through the rest of the course material. You may find it helpful to read it again when you come to revise for the exam. The accounts may remind you of what people say earlier in the course about more recent forms of care, other life experiences as well as discussions about community, environment, and who gives and receives care.

Study skills: Taking in history

What are you supposed to do with historical material? Should you try to remember all this information? Should you have taken some notes? Perhaps it is worth trying to pick out one or two developments to write down. One way is to write a few notes onto your wallchart. Then you will be fitting your new knowledge into the overall picture of the history of care which is gradually building up as you study K100 and highlight items on the wallchart. To be knowledgeable about care you don't need to remember masses of detailed history. But you do want to develop a kind of framework in your mind, so that you know roughly what the main developments have been, what sequence things happened in and a few key dates to act as pegs to hang other events around. After that, as you read more you can place new knowledge in context. Things become easier to understand and easier to remember.

Section 5
Empowerment and ethics

Talking to friends or sometimes to complete strangers about things we've done in our lives, is often a way of making social contact, of establishing our identity (you'll remember we discussed this in Unit 14). People offer parts of their life histories in exchange for other people's understanding and friendship. But that same talk can happen under rather different circumstances. You may have been asked to talk to someone about their past to help them make changes in their life, like leaving care or moving into new accommodation. How can you be sure that they are feeling comfortable telling you things about themselves? These issues are important to all of us but perhaps most important when it comes to talking and listening where there may be differences based on age, disability, race or gender, or a combination of any or all of these attributes.

We're going to look at two sets of issues: empowerment and ethics.

5.1 Empowerment in listening and talking

Talking about the past is often described as being an empowering process, changing power balances, enabling people to take power for themselves. Telling from experience can, as we saw in Unit 14, lift moods, alter depression and encourage sociability and a sense of self-identity. Yet interviewers – people who encourage the talk – often feel that they are in a more powerful position than the person they are interviewing. Indeed to 'empower' implies that power is something which one person is able to bestow on another – a rather contradictory notion given the meanings which empowerment is intended to evoke. Interviewers may think that they are better educated and that their experience of the research process gives them advantages. Class, disability, age, gender and race may all contribute to a sense of unequal powers. Researchers, particularly feminist researchers, have looked for ways to equalise the research relationship through approaches described as 'partnerships', that is ensuring that the person or people being researched share in all stages, having a say not only in how the interview is conducted but also the way the data are analysed and the results disseminated (Oakley, 1981; Gluck and Patai, 1991).

To achieve a sense of who feels empowered or disempowered may be a question of understanding the meaning of the interview for both parties. Dorothy Atkinson explains how, in her work with a group of older people with learning difficulties who were sharing their memories, she had to unlearn a perception she had of herself as a 'powerful woman':

> In retrospect, it seems obvious that group members had role models other than the powerful-woman image. She was my problem not theirs. Instead they related to me as their 'benefactor' in a variety of ways. Sometimes I was a friend, sometimes a co-conspirator, and sometimes just a 'young woman' who was interested in their stories. In the event I was more likely to be teased than deferred to, patronised rather than looked up to and even flirted with rather than feared. Nods, winks and smiles turned out to be more the order of the day than anxious looks.

(Atkinson, 1997, p. 36)

Perhaps more difficult to resolve than the question of power is the bias which researchers and interviewers place on the stories that they hear or expect interviewees to tell them. Younger people may have particular views and understandings of the past, so nostalgia for a lost past, or beliefs about a better future, may influence what people hear (Moody, 1988). A tendency to see people only as victims may also lead researchers to ask questions about experience of oppression and abuse when they might also be hearing about experiences of 'human resilience' and survival (Goodley, 1996).

How does power as an issue in interviews emerge through what is recorded in the Lennox Castle video?

Activity 13   Interview relationships

Allow about 15 minutes   In watching the video this time just focus on Howard Mitchell talking to James Lappin and Margaret Scally.

Watch these sequences and as you do make some notes about how you feel those interviews went. Listen out for any differences in the way James and Margaret respond and note the way Howard Mitchell poses his questions.

Comment   James Lappin talks about how he came to live in a hospital when he was 15 in 1925. He gives a very detailed account of the journey and how he was handed over. It may be that he's told this story many times before so he has a very polished account of what happened. On the other hand, it's also a very dramatic story, for him at least, one that is important to him and so is carefully told and with some authority. When he comes to talk about how he felt about it all then he becomes less certain, despite Howard pressing him to say more.

Margaret Scally talks about her work at the hospital and sounds assured as she gives her opinion about people she worked with and also how clothes were handed out in the morning. When Howard tries to get her to talk about relationships with staff, she is much less forthcoming: 'Some staff was good and some wasnae'. When pressed about this she says she 'Didn't bother with them' and goes on to explain punishment in terms of her being 'bad' and 'I was only a wee toddler'. However, she sounds more sure of herself when she comes to talk about the drugs she was given, describing taking them 'to try and help me calm down and that'.

Do you think there was a difference in how Margaret and James responded? Margaret is half James's age and she's also been living back in the community for six years. Though she's spent most of her life in institutions (she was only six when she first went in) she's had time to distance herself from the time she spent there and you may think that her interview shows signs of that. From her account we get a sense of someone who was treated very much as a 'bad girl', almost as if she had internalised infantilising treatment meted out to her by the nursing staff. In contrast, James Lappin seems quite deferential and eager to please. Perhaps these are the ways each learnt to cope during all those years.

Remember that, because this is a video, these interviews were more in the nature of a performance than a simple one-to-one discussion. Margaret Scally and James Lappin were being asked to talk about parts of their lives which must have evoked painful emotions and some anger, but perhaps the strong lights, cameras and all the people involved in making the video may have affected how they told their stories.

Howard Mitchell's questioning is skilful and gently probing but this is still a very public interview with people who knew him as a nurse. It's possible that for some of the time at least, they were telling him what they thought he wanted to hear. Remember in Reader Chapter 2 how he admits that: 'the most free and lurid criticism of the hospital and the nurses that I recorded was from an ex-patient who did not seem to grasp that I had worked there myself'.

It is important to remember about issues of power when we're listening to the way accounts are presented and stories told. You'll remember reading in Unit 15 about the ways group discussions can sometimes lead to consensus and compliance. But it may be that a direct response is not the most important matter. So, for example, when James Lappin responds to questions about his girlfriend by referring to his daily routine of walking to work we should perhaps be paying attention to what he's telling us about rules and the way he has become accustomed to other people making decisions about how he lives his life.

Study skills: What have you learnt from the video?

Does viewing the video feel any different from watching TV? What have you really learnt? Was it study time well spent?

In the Millmead section of the video you saw how 'reminiscence' work is used in a practical setting. No amount of printed description could have conveyed this situation – you were able to assess the level of interest of the participants, the quality of their memories, the group dynamics, the challenges faced by the facilitator. It is easy to read about the *ideas* behind reminiscence work – arguments for and against. But in just a few minutes a video recording can give you a much sharper insight into how well the ideas work in practice.

The Lennox Castle video took you inside an institution that may soon be closed down and which never offered easy access to outsiders. It is tremendously important to know about the history of institutional care and the lives of the many people involved. Yet it is very difficult to comprehend these lives without actually seeing and hearing the people. The way a person such as James Lappin or Margaret Scally sees and experiences the world is much easier to appreciate when you watch them speaking. But the video also teaches a lot very quickly about oral history as a method of research. You see the power of the oral evidence, the skills of asking questions, the weighty volumes of written records to be selected from, the atmosphere of the institution to be captured.

In fact the video is worth viewing many times. Information like this is hard to come by. But making the most of it does involve analytical skills. The more you become aware of what there is to look for, the more you will see. For example, if you watch just the James Lappin interview five times you will gain new insights each time – into how he understands the questions, how he puts together answers, how he makes sense of his life, how he relates to other people. Learning the social sciences is not just about absorbing ideas, it is learning how to look at the social world and how to analyse it. Video is excellent for that.

5.2 Ethical practice

Interviewing, asking people questions about themselves and their experience as many social workers, residential care staff and managers do, is more than just a chat or a conversation as we've seen. There's usually some broader purpose involved. It might be in connection with finding out about the past, but it could be part of getting someone ready for a move or a means to check out how prepared they are for some kind of change in their life. If there's some broader reason then it usually means that other people will also be interested in what's said and that a record of some kind will be kept. This raises the issue of what happens to what's recorded and whether the person being interviewed has any control over how things are managed. These are ethical issues about what is right and proper conduct in the circumstances.

Activity 14

Allow about 10 minutes

Drawing up guidelines

Imagine that someone has asked to talk to you about what you can remember of, say, your schooldays or an experience you had as a hospital patient, or perhaps when you first left home. What would you like to know about the interviewer and their project before they started? What kind of guarantees would you seek? Make some brief notes.

Comment

I can't know what issues you wanted to be clear about but here are some which occurred to me:

- I'd like to know what the interview is for.

- I'd like to know where I will be interviewed; my front room might not be my most relaxing environment, on the other hand anyone might walk into the kitchen and interrupt us.

- I'd expect to be treated in a friendly but not too familiar manner.

- I'd like to know what's going to happen to any notes or tapes made of what's said, where they are to be kept, who else might have access to them.

- I think I'd like some kind of written guarantee or agreement that I can sign about my preferences when it comes to storing a copy.

- I wouldn't mind having a copy of what was said, for my own peace of mind and perhaps to read later on to check for mistakes I may have made.

At one level what's listed here is simply good practice in interpersonal communication – what might be described as polite and considerate behaviour. But at another level there are some quite important issues here about what the outcomes of an interview are and what rights an interviewee has over what is recorded. What we've drawn up here could be a draft set of guidelines for good practice in interviewing. You might like to try them or your own list out on someone to see if there's anything they would add to the list. For example, if you showed them the list above they might add that on some matters they'd prefer to be interviewed by someone of the same gender, or they'd always prefer to be interviewed in their own language. You'll be coming back to these issues again in Unit 19 in relation to questions raised by record making and record keeping.

What we've considered so far are situations where we're happy and agree with what's going on. Consent arises as an issue most often in relation to medical interventions like operations when patients have to sign a form which allows the surgeon to make incisions when they're not able to say whether they agree or not. Of course we expect to be fully briefed beforehand about what's going to happen to our bodies when we're not conscious. As long as we understand what the surgeon's talking about, and this may not always be easy, then signing consent is a reasonably straightforward procedure, but it is always one that involves a degree of trust.

But, what if someone doesn't find it easy to understand what's going on? Obtaining a signature from someone, or their proxy, may not be a problem; what is more difficult is to be certain that the person whose consent has been gained understands what they have given consent to. This is the issue of 'informed consent'.

People researching in the area of learning disability have worked with different strategies. Booth and Booth describe how they approached research with 'the guiding principle of self-advocacy':

> that *'people with learning difficulties are people first'* and with *'a fundamental tenet of the citizen advocacy movement'* that *'the advocate (or, in our case, the researcher) treats the interests of their partner (here, the research subject) as if they were their own'*. (1994, p. 24)

The strategy they adopted was to use an intermediary who was known to the people they wanted to interview. This person was asked to explain the reasons for the research and to ask if the potential subjects would be willing to meet the researchers. This had the advantage of making it easier for people to refuse but there was a problem that the interviewers might seem distant and so be associated with authority.

Explaining procedures to people who may not easily understand or be familiar with the context you work in can also present challenges. People who are not able to read or write cannot be left with pieces of text to look at or for others to read to them, however sensitively these are presented. It may be necessary to use other approaches, pictures or sketches for example, both to explain the process and to provide a record of what has been discussed. For an example, see the information sheet overleaf. Jan Walmsley prepared this sheet when she was carrying out her study of 22 adults with learning difficulties and their experiences of care and caring (Reader Chapter 4).

Issues of empowerment and ethics are important, not just in research situations, but in any context where someone may be asked to participate in an activity which isn't familiar to them. We've used research as an example, but you could substitute it with preparing someone for an assessment, introducing someone to a new environment or finding out what someone understands about a new service or how they spend their leisure time. It's a matter of listening and facilitating communication by taking the time to make your intentions clear while giving someone else the time to explain in a way that suits them best.

What's it like?

Good    *or* OK    *or* Not so good

How?

I will come to meet you with my tape recorder and talk
with you about these things: you tell me your story,
You can invite someone else along: a friend

  staff

  parent

You can choose where we meet
You can choose when we meet

How long?

Once or twice or three times for about one hour

What will happen to the information

You will get:

  a tape recording of our talk

  your 'story'

  a 'life map' of your life

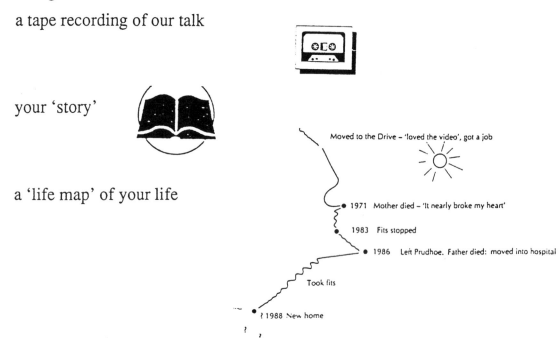

An information sheet prepared by Jan Walmsley for respondents to her 'What it's like to care' research project.

Key points

- Interviewing people should involve being aware of their rights and preferences.

- Talking about the past has been described as empowering but differences of age, gender, disability and ethnicity may lead to inequalities between interviewer and interviewee which interviewers need to be sensitive to.

- Sometimes it's more important to listen to *how* people are talking than to check *what* they say for accuracy or relevance.

- Gaining consent must be at the heart of any interview, whatever its purpose. However being certain that consent is 'informed' may take time and require creative approaches.

Section 6
From institutions to residential care

We've spent some time looking at one institution as a basis for understanding how these large-scale living arrangements emerged and persisted. This has taken us back in time and has also raised issues about what happens when we involve other people in finding out about the past. To end this unit we're going back to institutions again, linking what we've read about institutions to issues raised by ethics and empowerment in the context of current debates about the future of institutional living.

Although most of the large long-stay hospitals are now scheduled for closure and people are returning to live 'in the community' their story is not yet quite over. As the closure programme draws to an end, the debate about the nature of long-term care has become more heated. In some areas, campaigns to keep at least part of hospital grounds open, with special accommodation for people with greatest needs, is leading to delays and some quite bitter struggles, not just about the land and its use but also about the nature of appropriate care, particularly for people with learning difficulties and mental health problems. As you read you might like to compare the different interests represented today with those who took up positions for and against residential care in the 1950s and 1960s. Fifty years later some new groups are involved.

The two functions of institutions – care and segregation – are still a feature of debates. Within mental health, discussions about institutional care have been fuelled by funding shortages and administrative breakdowns which have had tragic consequences. The result is that public debates have focused more on risk and safety, with policy leaning towards a continuation of a limited amount of secure provision, evoking the original notion of asylum as a source of protection and withdrawal from society. It's not clear who is supposed to benefit most from such arrangements, society at large or people experiencing mental distress who, as members of the organisation Survivors Speak Out, have criticised not only institutions but the drugs-based treatment associated with them. As far as institutional child care is concerned, and we've given little attention to the history of that form of provision here, this has had a very bad press. Accounts of abuse as well as officially sanctioned forms of restraint have left residential child care with an uncertain future.

A different voice enters the debate where care and support for people with learning difficulties or older people are concerned. Here the private provider plays a powerful part, with their vested interest in care as a business. It's perhaps in relation to learning disability with its history of segregated communities and institutions like Lennox Castle as well as the late twentieth century emergence of representative organisations that the battle lines over the future of institutional care are clearly drawn.

Parents push for village life

Two research studies have opened the debate on residential villages for people with learning difficulties.

Parents of people with learning difficulties are putting pressure on ministers to expand the provision of village communities.

(Community Care, 20–26 June 1996)

Peers laud villages

Village communities for people with learning difficulties have supporters in the House of Lords

An angry debate about the role of 'village' communities in services for people with learning difficulties has erupted in the House of Lords. This will worry many of those who support more integrationist approaches to community care, since peers who favour village communities have tended to dominate.

(Community Care, 23–29 January 1997)

Government open to idea of villages

Social services chiefs are querying the government's apparent backing of village communities for people with learning difficulties.

(Community Care, 18–24 July 1996)

Government boost for village life

The government has made a shift towards supporting village communities for people with learning difficulties.

(Community Care, 4–10 July 1996)

RESCARE, an organisation representing families of people with learning difficulties, has no doubts about the need for 'village communities' to carry on existing.

Families and family burden are at the heart of the RESCARE argument:

> *RESCARE families wish their handicapped members to be nurtured in a life style with purposeful, stimulating, daily activity, including recreation and companionship with their peers and sympathetic staff. They desire the systematic development of each person's potential. They see integration with the community as a desirable adjunct rather than the primary objective of care, and they abhor the use of their handicapped relatives as pawns in an ideological battle in which living in 'the community' takes priority over freedom of choice and other forms of care which they know to be more suitable for their loved ones.*

(Cox and Pearson, 1995, p. 3)

Values into Action takes a contrasting position:

> *Village communities! That is now the rallying cry of the institutional lobby. If most mental handicap hospitals cannot be saved, then the next best thing (from their perspective) must be the 'village community'. Having lost the argument of first choice they are marshalling their forces behind their second choice: to transplant the institutional environment into the late twentieth century without losing the essence of institutions.*

This desperate last-ditch stand is not perhaps a surprising move for people who sneeringly accuse others of 'political correctness' for promoting the rights of people with learning difficulties. It seems they are unable to accept that people with learning difficulties have the right to be treated with dignity and respect within a society to which they fully belong.

(Values into Action, 1995, p. 1)

Mencap takes a midway position, arguing for diversity of provision, but based on the primacy of diversity of needs, interests and wishes. As a spokesman pointed out:

The arguments that have been put forward for the village community model are very close indeed to the original arguments for setting up the hospitals ... only the architecture of the solution is different ... There has to be a very strong argument for depriving those residents of what most of the rest of us want, and the great majority of people with even the most severe disabilities now enjoy – a home in the community.

(Personal communication)

Researchers into provision found some interesting features in all the diverse forms of care available, including 'domiciliary support to people in their own homes; adult fostering or family placement; supported lodging; staffed and unstaffed group homes; hostels; residential communities; village communities; specialised health facilities, nursing homes and hospitals'. They found that:

- *... smaller community-based group homes are associated with better performance and more positive outcomes than either larger community-based hostels or NHS Mental Handicap Hospitals. Such positive differences in outcomes have been found for people with severe and profound learning disabilities, people with multiple disabilities and people with seriously challenging behaviour.*

- *... that significant variation exists in the quality and costs of all types of services ... for a significant minority of people in smaller community-based group homes, their quality of life is indistinguishable from the generally poor quality of life people experience in NHS mental handicap hospitals.*

- *... on many measures of outcome (e.g. choice, income, employment, friendships) the quality of life of people with learning disabilities in all settings is impoverished when compared to the general population.*

(Emerson et al., 1996, pp. 15–16)

As this unit was being completed we heard that James Lappin was being prepared for a move into the community. Given his apparent acceptance of life at Lennox Castle and an impression that, in old age, he feels secure in that environment, you probably agree that his move back to Glasgow raises some interesting issues for James, his relatives and the care workers who support him.

Conclusion

As the debates continue, history seems to have a role to play. Putting our own convictions, prejudices and philosophies to the test of time by identifying continuities and changes, we may find ways towards a more reflective and critical approach to provision and practice for health and social care. For example, we may assume that the kind of practices which were a feature of life at Lennox Castle will disappear as these large institutions disappear, but is that really possible? Think back to the care workers at Cedar Court whom you read about in Unit 8. Are there some continuities in practice and attitudes there?

We began the unit with three core questions. You might like to look back at them now. In answering them we have:

- included an overview of the history of institutional care in general and considered why there was pressure for change
- taken a look at the history of one institution as a way towards understanding how one form of care came to be provided in the past
- looked at the debates about institutional care today and the interests of the different protagonists
- looked at different sources of evidence about the past and how these complement each other
- considered issues of power and ethics in interviewing people, using the example of oral history.

In the next two blocks you will be going on to discuss issues of power and control, evidence taking, account making and organisational life inside and outside institutions and within a wide range of caring relationships. As you work through, think back to the history we've uncovered in this unit. However distant and separate the past may seem, however different the language and the forms of provision, the next two blocks raise the questions of how far care practice has changed today and of how we might want it to change in the future.

References

Alaszewski, A. (1986) *Institutional Care and the Mentally Handicapped: The Mental Handicap Hospital*, Croom Helm, London.

Atkinson, D. (1997) *An Auto/biographical Approach to Learning Disability Research*, Ashgate, Aldershot.

Binney, M. (1995) 'Introduction' in Philips, E. *Mind Over Matter: A Study of the Country's Threatened Mental Asylums*, SAVE Britain's Heritage, pp. 1–8.

Booth, T. and Booth, W. (1994) *Parenting Under Pressure: Mothers and Fathers with Learning Difficulties*, Open University Press, Buckingham

Cox, C. and Pearson, M. (1995) *Made to Care: The Case for Residential and Village Communities for People with a Mental Handicap*, RESCARE, Stockport.

Dickens, C. (1858) *Barnaby Rudge: A Tale of the Riots of Eighty*, Chapman and Hall, London.

Dyson, B. (1994) *Liberty in Britain 1934–1991*, Civil Liberties Trust, London.

Emerson, E., Cullen, C., Hatton, C. and Cross, B. (1996) *Residential Provision for People with Learning Disabilities: Summary Report*, Hester Adrian Research Centre, Manchester.

Evers, H. (1993) 'The development of geriatric medicine' in Johnson, J. and Slater, R. (eds) *Ageing and Later Life*, Sage, London.

Fido, R. and Potts, M. (1989) ' "It's not true what was written down!": experiences of life in a mental handicap institution' *Oral History*, Vol. 17, No. 2, pp. 31–34.

Gladstone, D. (1996) 'The changing dynamic of insitutional care' in Digby, A. and Wright, D. (eds) *From Idiocy to Mental Deficicency*, Routledge, London.

Gluck, S.B. and Patai, D. (eds) (1991) *Women's Words: The Feminist Practice of Oral History*, Routledge, London.

Goddard, J. (1996) *Mixed Feelings: Littlemore Hospital – An Oral History Project*, Oxfordshire County Council Leisure & Arts.

Goodley, D. (1996) 'Tales of hidden lives: a critical examination of life history research with people who have learning difficulties', *Disability and Society*, Vol. 11, No. 3, pp. 333–48.

Hendrick, H. (1994) *Child Welfare: England 1872-1969*, Routledge, London.

Humphries, S. and Gordon, P. (1992) *Out of Sight: The Experience of Disability 1900-1950*, Northcote House, Plymouth.

Hurt, J.S. (1988) *Outside the Mainstream: A History of Special Education*, Batsford, London.

Ignatieff, M. (1983) 'Total institutions and working classes: a review essay', *History Workshop Journal*, Spring 1983, pp. 167–73.

Jackson, M. (1996) 'Institutional provision for the feeble-minded in Edwardian England: Sandlebridge and the scientific morality of permanent care', in Digby, A. and Wright, D. (eds) *From Idiocy to Mental Deficiency*, Routledge, London.

Jackson, M. (1997) 'Images from the past: using photographs' in Atkinson, D., Jackson, M. and Walmsley, J. *Exploring the History of Learning Disability*, BILD (British Institute of Learning Disability), Kidderminster.

Jones, K. and Fowles, A.J. (1984) *Ideas on Institutions: Analysing the Literature on Long-term Care and Custody*, Routledge & Kegan Paul, London.

Moody, H.R. (1988) 'Twenty-five years of life-review', *Journal of Gerontological Social Work*, Vol. 12 (3/4), pp. 7–24.

Nolan, P. (1993) *A History of Mental Health Nursing*, Chapman Hall, London.

Oakley, A. (1981) 'Interviewing women: a contradiction in terms' in Roberts, H. (ed.) *Doing Feminist Research*, Routledge & Kegan Paul, London.

Ponting, C. (1992) 'Churchill's plan for racial purity', *Guardian*, 20 June.

Robb, B. (1967) *Sans Everything: A Case to Answer*, Nelson, London.

Ryan, J. and Thomas, F. (1987) *The Politics of Mental Handicap*, Free Association Books, London.

Thompson, P. (1988) *The Voice of the Past*, Oxford University Press, Oxford.

Timmins, N. (1996) *The Five Giants: A Biography of the Welfare State*, Fontana, London.

Townsend, P. (1962) *The Last Refuge: A Survey of Residential Institutions and Homes for the Aged*, Routledge & Kegan Paul, London.

Values into Action (1995) 'Re-cycling Arguments and Institutions', *Values into Action Newsletter*, 81, Summer.

Williams, F. (1989) *Social Policy: A Critical Introduction*, Polity Press, Cambridge.

Wright, D. (1996) ' "Childlike in his innocence" Lay attitudes to "idiots" and "imbeciles" in Victorian England', in Digby, A. and Wright, D. (eds) *From Idiocy to Mental Deficiency*, Routledge, London.

Wright, D. and Digby, A. (1996) (eds) *From Idiocy to Mental Deficiency*, Routledge, London.

Acknowledgements

Grateful acknowledgement is made to the following sources for permission to reproduce material in this unit:

Text

'Shot in the arm for former hospitals', *Hampstead and Highgate Express*, 7th February 1997; 'Trouble at Lennox Castle', *Kirkintilloch Herald*, January 1956; 'Lennox Castle riot inquiry', *Kirkintilloch Herald*, 1st February 1956.

Illustrations

P. 112: CF 3612 The Thomas Coram Foundling Hospital, c. 1746 by Richard Wilson (1714–82). Coram Foundation, London/Bridgeman Art Library, London; *p. 113*: Artwork courtesy of Knight, Frank and Rutley; *p. 116*: Courtesy of the Northumberland County Archives Service/ Northumberland Mental Health NHS Trust, St George's Hospital, Morpeth; *p. 117*: Oxfordshire County Council Archives; *p.121*: © Howard Mitchell; *p. 123*: Greater Glasgow Health Board Archive; *p. 127 (top)*: Mary Evans Picture Library; *p. 127 (bottom)*: Courtesy Friends' House Library; *p. 128*: MENCAP's Hidden Histories Photo Collection; p. 131 (top): By courtesy of Edinburgh City Libraries; *p. 131 (bottom)*: Barnardo's Photographic and Film Archive; *pp. 137, 142 (top left and right)*: Colin Sproul; *p. 140*: Courtesy Brynmor Jones Library, University of Hull; *p. 142 (centre left and right)*: Margaret Scally; *p. 142 (bottom left and right)*: James Lappin; *p. 151*: Courtesy of the Waltham Forest Oral History Workshop, London Borough of Waltham Forest; *p. 158*: Jan Walmsley.

Unit 17
Developing Skills in Communication

Prepared for the course team by Joanna Bornat

While you are working on Unit 17, you will need:
- Course Reader
- Offprints Book
- *The Good Study Guide*
- Pathways VQ Guide
- Care in the UK
- Skills video

Contents

Introduction

Unit 17 focuses on:

- supporting effective communication
- facilitating the communication of sensitive issues
- managing communication within a group
- working with numbers
- developing writing skills.

Communication is at the heart of health and social care. This has been demonstrated throughout Block 4. In the audio and video cassettes alone you have:

- heard Jamie Knight and Sarah Burrows, his former social worker, talking together about making his life story
- seen Howard Mitchell using his skills as a nurse and as a researcher talking to Colin Sproul, Margaret Scally and James Lappin about their experiences of life in Lennox Castle
- heard in Paul Theobald's account of his life the great value of communication networks between AIDS sufferers
- seen a group of older people at Millmead Linked Service Centre meeting to talk together and share memories.

In the printed text, for example, John Killick described his work in a nursing home, listening to people with dementia and helping them produce written life histories. And the Duffy and McCarthy chapter in the Reader described intensive communications in weekly group meetings with young women in a hostel.

Block 4 has looked at why knowing about communication is important within care contexts.

- Unit 14 showed the importance of being able to communicate your life experiences to others. It explored ways that opportunities for this can be built into care strategies.
- Unit 15 highlighted the fact that care is often provided in group settings and examined how communications within groups can help or hinder care work.
- Unit 16 showed how differently the past is communicated through oral accounts as opposed to official written records. In the case of institutional living, it showed how important it is – given the power of institutions to define and dominate – to enable ordinary people to communicate their experiences to the world in their own words.

Central themes of the unit

As you can see, the topic of communication within different care contexts is a huge one. To make it manageable and to maintain an emphasis on skills, Unit 17 focuses on four key points of good practice:

Key points

Good practice in communication means:

- supporting effective communication
- facilitating the communication of sensitive issues
- managing communication within a group.

But through each of these three there also runs a more general aspect of communicating skill:

- developing an awareness of how your own behaviour may empower or disempower the people you are seeking to help and support.

Like the other skills units (5, 9 and 13) this unit provides activities which should enable you to build up evidence of what you can do in a portfolio. If you want help in mapping the VQ areas onto what is in this unit then you should check through the Pathways VQ Guide which accompanies the course.

The unit uses two video scenes and a written case study, 'Lunch-time at East View', in which a group of under-fives with special needs sit down to lunch with their day care worker.

Unit 17 video content

Scene 8 'Communicating experience': older people with learning difficulties tell their stories of life in an institution.

Scene 9 'Private talk in a public space': a care worker, portrayed by an actor, finds a way to tell an elderly man living in residential care (also an actor) about his imminent prostate operation.

Section 1

Challenges of communicating in care contexts

Communication is sharing meaning.
(Kelly, 1981)

This definition by a philosopher is as useful as any. Communication is central both to our personal lives as human beings and also to the ways human societies work. Communicating is something most people are doing most of the time – often without noticing. But are there special issues about communicating in health and social care contexts? We can answer this by looking back at Units 14, 15 and 16.

Activity 1   **Skills of communicating in care contexts**

Allow about 15 minutes   Below are some examples of communications within a care context taken from Block 4. In each case, think carefully about what is said to whom and why, and what might be difficult or sensitive. Then for each, write down some *special communication skills* you think the carers involved would need.

If you made notes while you were watching, listening or reading, find them and see whether they trigger any ideas.

Unit 14:   Sarah Burrows communicating with Jamie Knight.
John Killick writing life histories with dementia sufferers.

Unit 15:   Weekly meetings in the hostel for young women.
Kavita Kohli working with the group of Asian deaf women.
Gary Baker and the reminiscence group at Millmead.

Unit 16:   Howard Mitchell talking to James Lappin and Margaret Scally.

Comment   Some of the people you saw find it difficult to take part in communicating without help and support. Here are some of the special communication skills and techniques I noted.

Signing: Some people experience a physical impairment such as deafness. To communicate with her group of Asian women Kavita Kohli needs to be skilled in signing.

Careful listening: Some of the older people at Millmead speak quietly and indistinctly, so Gary Baker has to concentrate carefully on what they say and repeat some things to be sure that everyone in the group can follow. James Lappin at Lennox Castle also speaks indistinctly and cannot always find words for what he wants to say, so Howard Mitchell has to listen carefully for the general meaning – and ask a follow up question if he isn't sure. Although we don't hear John Killick in action, he must have developed similar skills to piece together the accounts of people with dementia.

Positioning: To have a group of people working successfully together, when some speak quietly and others have hearing loss, Gary Baker must give careful attention to how people are positioned in relation to each other. He will also have to direct his voice appropriately for anyone with a hearing aid, and turn to face those who find lip movements helpful.

Straightforward language: Howard Mitchell is interviewing people with learning difficulties so he has to use an appropriate range of words and concepts. Similarly, when Jamie Knight was a child Sarah Burrows must have had to discuss very difficult issues in suitably straightforward words and language.

Empathetic listening: Howard Mitchell, Gary Baker, John Killick and Sarah Burrows all need to talk to people about very personal experiences which might sometimes be painful or embarrassing, or trigger sudden emotional reactions. They need to be able to listen with understanding and sympathy, and give support at appropriate times. They also need to be able to encourage people who lack confidence that other people will value what they say. (Empathy means trying to 'project' yourself into the other person's situation and experience, in order to understand them as fully as possible.)

Using prompts: Gary Baker found that less confident people and those with impairments such as deafness and memory loss seemed to respond well to objects being passed round or certain words or songs or photographs. Sarah Burrows also used photographs and took Jamie to places he remembered when she was helping him to talk about his feelings and his past.

Drawing pictures, making things: People working with children who are being adopted or fostered use approaches such as asking them to draw pictures and make things, to explore with them their feelings and understanding of what is happening to them. Sarah Burrows used working with Jamie Knight on his life history book to help them communicate about these very difficult experiences. In the video, Gary Baker showed the life story book which one of the day centre users had made.

Using games: When we were recording the audio tape Sarah Burrows also mentioned a game she played with Jamie:

> *We put some coloured water in a jam jar, that's when you were going through a really prickly stage and you didn't want to let anybody in or let anyone talk to you or be friendly with you, and so I covered a jam jar and we put some coloured water in it and covered it up with clingfilm, and then tipped it upside down and then tried to pour water on and I was showing you that by you putting this skin on no one could get to you and you quite liked it cos you were shaking it and putting water on the top.*

Using games like these helps children to talk about their emotions in a way that feels safe for them (Ryan and Walker, 1993, p. 22).

Sharing control: In contrast to the other cases, the main communication difficulties in the hostel arose from the sharp differences between the 'youth subculture' shared by the young women and the 'caring subculture' of the staff. The weekly meetings attempted to bridge the gap, but this involved staff in withdrawing to a considerable extent from exercising control over the meetings. Staff wanted to use group communication to encourage the young women to 'verbalise conflicts' instead of acting them out – and to reflect together on their behaviour, their experiences and their aims in life in a way that facilitated personal growth. But they could not approach these issues directly. They had to develop skills of hanging back and making only occasional strategic interventions.

All these are special skills which we have seen in action in Block 4. But like other skills you meet in K100, they are much more than a matter of proficient technique. These skills need to be developed in ways which are consistent with the five principles of good practice outlined in Unit 5. Communications within a care context should:

- enable people to develop their own potential
- enable people to have a voice and be heard
- respect people's beliefs and preferences
- promote and support people's rights to appropriate services
- respect people's privacy and rights to confidentiality.

Activity 2
Allow about 10 minutes

Principles of good practice in communicating in care contexts

Go back to the cases we have been looking at and think about:

(a) whether you can see the five principles demonstrated in the communications we have observed

(b) where you can see any danger of failing to meet these principles.

Jot down some thoughts on both of these points.

Comment

Here are just a few suggestions:

(a) (i) Sarah Burrows, John Killick and Gary Baker are all working with people's life histories, with a view to developing their potential. Similarly, the weekly discussions in the hostel for young women were intended to have a 'therapeutic' effect – helping them through adolescent development.

(ii) A key purpose of Howard Mitchell's oral history work and John Killick's written histories is to help give a voice to people who have often been overlooked.

(iii) John Killick is very concerned to present people's life histories in a way that reflects their own beliefs and preferences.

(iv) Sarah Burrows spent many hours communicating with Jamie when he was young, so that she could support him in getting appropriate care.

(v) She also made sure that the life history was under his control, so that he decided what went into it and who got to see it. Similarly, Howard Mitchell is very concerned about issues of confidentiality in handling the information he elicits from the people he interviews. Mel Channing emphasises that looking at the life history books must be 'all confidential of course'.

In other words the cases we chose for Block 4 generally show communications that display the five principles of good practice (which is why we chose them).

But notice that the link between communication and the five principles works both ways. Not only should the five principles underpin communication practice – the five principles are themselves underpinned by effective communication. How can people's potential be developed, other than through communication with others? Without the ability to communicate how can people have a voice and be heard? How can you respect people's beliefs and preferences except by sensitive asking and listening? How can people's rights to appropriate services be promoted without effective communication? And people's rights to privacy and confidentiality are all about recognising limits as to what should be communicated to whom.

So effective communication and the five principles are closely bound up with each other. But what about the dangers?

(b)   (i)   Done insensitively, the kind of work John Killick was undertaking with confused patients could easily become intrusive, disorientating and patronising – stunting rather than helping develop their potential.

       (ii)   Gary Baker could easily dominate discussion in the reminiscence group and make assumptions which smother people's attempts to give voice to their personal experiences.

       (iii)   With her group of Asian deaf women Kavita Kohli might slip into assuming that they all experience similar degrees of impairment and that their main interest is traditional Asian activities and customs.

       (iv)   In the young women's hostel, discussing issues in a group setting could mean that some individuals' needs for particular kinds of services get overlooked, because they do not fit within the 'world-view' developed by the larger group.

       (v)   In the kind of work Sarah Burrows did with a child such as Jamie Knight, there is a very difficult line between communications that are appropriate to pass on (say, to foster parents) and what is confidential.

Dangers such as these highlight the need to beware of ways of communicating which make people feel less equal, less respected or diminished in any way. In working with frail older people, for example, we should find ways to communicate warmth and support without resorting to language which is infantilising like 'good girl' or using a first name before checking out what someone wishes to be called. Similarly, work with young children means avoiding patronising and clichéd questions about schools and teachers instead of letting the communication begin gradually so that the child is able to respond in the way they want to, without being forced or overwhelmed by the adult.

So, although we have noted some special communication skills needed by care workers, it is important not to put too much emphasis on the 'specialness'. Supportiveness and sensitivity have to be carefully balanced against respect and equality. It is easy to patronise or exclude people by communicating in ways that underestimate their abilities – as in the famous phrase 'Does he take sugar?' Service users and care workers are first and foremost fellow human beings. Communication – the *sharing* of meaning – lies at the heart of life in a society and involves us all. In care contexts the basic rules of normal communication should apply.

Key points

- Communication is sharing meaning.
- Sometimes communication needs to be supported by special skills.
- Good practice in communication means:
    - being supportive
    - enabling people to have a voice and be heard
    - making sure that beliefs and preferences are respected
    - ensuring that people get appropriate care while respecting rights to privacy.

Section 2
Supporting effective communication

My first video sequence focuses on how communication in care contexts can be supported. But first we need to consider *why* communication needs supporting.

2.1 Barriers to communication

When communications are difficult it is often because of 'barriers' of one kind or another.

Activity 3 | **Identifying barriers**

Allow about 10 minutes | Think back to occasions when you have experienced difficulty communicating with someone. Can you identify any barriers to communication which contributed to the difficulty?

Down the side of a sheet of paper write the headings – physical environment, disability and impairment, attitudes, differences, and emotions and feelings. Then write down the barriers you thought of, under the most appropriate heading. Add any more barriers you can think of.

Comment | I thought of occasions when communications were difficult because of:

Physical environment:

- building design
- loud music
- sheer physical distance.

At a basic level the physical environment may be a major obstruction to communication. People cannot communicate if they can't actually make contact with other people because there is no transport suitable for wheelchairs, or a building has no lifts, ramps or automatic doors. And beyond the issue of access, there is the quality of the physical environment. Noise, lack of privacy and interruptions are also barriers to communication in their own way. On a larger scale a whole area can inhibit communications, as with the isolated landscape in which Lennox Castle Hospital was built and its designed segregation of men from women.

Disability and impairment:

- a person's deafness
- loss of memory for language
- a speech impediment.

In fact, many disabled people argue that it is not disability which prevents communication but society's unwillingness to promote access or support communication. So, some deaf people argue that hearing impairment is not the main barrier, but rather the slowness of people with hearing to develop an ability to communicate in the language of deaf people – sign language.

Nevertheless, differences based on impairment need to be identified if they are not to become barriers to communication. This means that care workers should be trained to recognise the influence of hearing impairment, limited mobility, visual and verbal impairments and cognitive difference such as memory loss and learning disability.

Attitudes:

* deferential attitudes to professionals
* ageist attitudes
* lack of respect for other people's culture and ethnicity.

We talked earlier about ageist attitudes embedded in the way people speak. Assumptions about the values and feelings of older and younger people can also act as barriers. So automatically speaking loudly to an older person may not always be helpful and may convey a quite negative impression. Stereotyped thinking can deflect you from seeing someone as an individual with particular life experiences and interests and so prevent effective communication. It can also become a 'self-fulfilling prophecy' in that the person may come to internalise your negative stereotyping – developing low self-esteem and an unwillingness to speak up and be assertive.

Differences:

* language difference
* differences in customs
* differences in life experience as between young people and older people.

Lack of a shared language is obviously a major barrier to communication. But even with some shared language, cultural differences can give rise to misunderstandings. Terms like 'passing water', or 'breaking wind' are mystifying if translated word for word, and a concept such as 'healthy eating' may have very different connotations within different cultural groups. It's important to be aware of and respond to differences of age, disability and gender, for example preference for same sex professional care may prevent some women from seeking help when they feel they can't expect to find a woman nurse or doctor.

Emotions and feelings:

* aggressive behaviour
* distress.

Distress or anger can prevent someone from making an initial approach for help or may overwhelm someone to the extent that they are scarcely able to interact with others at all.

2.2 Overcoming barriers

Identifying barriers is the first step. The next is to work out ways of overcoming them.

For example, it is important to choose a physical environment which is accessible physically. But it also needs to provide the right surroundings for communication to be effective. The 'accessible' entrance hall, lounge, cafeteria, or busy office is no substitute for a quiet and private meeting place where someone is able to express their feelings and be heard. If a person seems quiet and withdrawn, the first steps to communication may involve building confidence and trust. John Killick's work with people with dementing illnesses is one example of encouraging older people to feel confident enough to talk even when they feel insecure about their identity and their ability to remember and summon up words.

Where a person has a speech, hearing or sight impairment, it is important to be aware of ways of supporting communication, such as:

- signing in British Sign Language or Makaton
- using Braille screen readers and screen magnification for computer-based information
- induction loops to support hearing in public areas
- possum as an aid to controlling their environment and as an aid to speech for people who are paralysed
- 'Hearing dogs for the Deaf'
- 'Guide dogs for the Blind'.

Overcoming barriers to communication in K100

The OU offers a range of support to students with communication difficulties. These include supplying the course in audio cassette form to students with visual impairments, supplying transcripts of cassette material to students with hearing difficulties, and making special arrangements for examinations for some students. These are all available to K100 students. In planning the course we also took advice on typefaces and design features which would make the material easier to read. And in the K100 videos you may have noticed another attempt to overcome barriers to communication. Can you recall it?

Speech on the videos is subtitled. We felt that this would help when you are listening to someone with a speech impairment – especially if this is combined with the 'cultural difference' of a strong regional accent with which you may not be familiar. However, we felt it was then important to subtitle everyone, without exception, since selective subtitling might have the effect of exaggerating an apparent difference, and so reinforce attitudes that in themselves discourage communication. (Effective communication is about being inclusive and facilitative.) As well as clarifying speech, subtitles can help to reinforce visual images which are unfamiliar or unclear. So, whether or not you yourself have a hearing impairment, you may have found the subtitling useful.

2.3 Identifying effective strategies in communication

You are now going to look at a short video sequence. This features a group of older people with learning difficulties talking to a psychologist, Maggie Potts, about how they came to be residents at a large hospital in the north of England. Their age and background means that their experiences are similar to those of James Lappin at Lennox Castle. Although the details of the events they describe are very interesting, your task is to focus on the way the stories are communicated.

Activity 4   **Communicating experience**

Allow about 20 minutes

Get ready to play Scene 8 of the skills video. You will see the following people:

- Lorraine Day, Deputy Leisure and Recreation Officer
- Evelyn King, resident of the hospital
- Mary Brayshay, resident of the hospital
- Rebecca Fido, research worker
- Douglas Holmes, resident of the hospital

First just watch and take in what is happening. Then rewind the tape and watch it again. As you watch, make some notes under two headings:

(a) Potential barriers to communication (use the same checklist as before, to help you look out for different kinds of barriers – physical environment, disability and impairment, attitudes, differences, and emotions and feelings).

(b) Communication being supported (make a list of the participants and look for ways each supports the communications of others).

Comment   (a) **Potential barriers to communication.** I noted:

Physical environment: the interviews were held in a public place (a hospital) and in front of an audience (the film production crew and others involved in making the video). Also, the video cameras have imposed a rather unnatural line up. Normally in an interview two people would face each other or turn partly towards each other. The wheelchairs and people's impairments do make a difference to the amount of freedom they have to shift around during the interview and, for example, choose their preferred eye level.

Disability and impairment: Mary has a speech impediment and Douglas, Evelyn and Mary are all wheelchair users.

Differences: differences between professionals and clients; differences of gender and of disability; and differences between being an interviewer and an interviewee.

(b) **Communication being supported.** I noted:

Lorraine Day sits close to Evelyn, uses eye contact and lowers her voice when Evelyn talks quietly. When she is speaking Lorraine is listening and responding to Evelyn's emotional expression. She waits for Mary to speak even though she has some difficulty understanding what she says. She uses straightforward and uncomplicated words and language.

Evelyn King also draws close to Lorraine. She underlines the points she wants to make with gestures and slow emphatic statements. She facilitates Mary's communication by interpreting for her, explaining what she says to Lorraine, but she also lets Mary talk and doesn't interrupt her or talk over her.

Mary Brayshay. I wasn't sure that she supported anyone else's communication. However she did facilitate the interview to the extent that she took her turn and didn't interrupt when Evelyn was telling her story.

Rebecca Fido kept eye contact as she talked to Douglas Holmes showing him that she was listening. She communicated respect and she encouraged him to bring out the details of how he learnt to read and write with gentle probing questions.

Douglas Holmes. Because of his position and possibly the effect of his impairment it wasn't easy for him to keep eye contact; however he compensated by choosing his words carefully and explaining carefully the opportunities he grasped in order to learn to read and write as a young child. Clearly verbal communication has always been important to him.

In the video sequence we see both care workers and service users using skills of effective communication as they talk and listen. It is a reciprocal process, one in which good practice is being demonstrated and responded to on both sides. The result is some powerful story-telling.

In this video sequence we see a well-planned set of exchanges. The care workers presumably made specific preparations to ensure that the interview objectives were met. We now focus on this preparatory stage to communication.

Activity 5   **Preparing for communication**

Allow about 15 minutes   Imagine you are Lorraine, who works at the hospital as the deputy leisure and recreation officer. You need to know the residents' views about the programmes you've been running. You want some of the volunteers who help with your recreational programme to find out by interviewing residents. You've done a lot of training of the volunteers in the past, including in communication skills. Now you need to prepare them for this particular enquiry.

What guidance will you need to give them? How should they set up the interviews? How should they conduct them? What kind of difficulties or misunderstandings might arise? Make a list of the skills you think your volunteers will need in order to find out what you want to know.

Comment   **Establishing a clear role:** You want the volunteers to be aware of their role in relationship to the residents and the project and to communicate this to the residents. They should be friendly but not too familiar. They should be clear about what the interview is for. If they are asked for advice, or if someone uses the interview to make a complaint, then they should find out who else the interviewee would be prepared to talk to before taking things further. Volunteers may hear things which are upsetting. They will need to recognise if they are getting too involved. And they will need to know how to manage their own feelings if someone becomes distressed or angry.

Being sensitive to preferences about being talked to: The volunteers should find out how each resident prefers to be addressed.

Checking out and removing barriers: Volunteers will need to check out the spaces where they'll be talking to the residents. They'll need to be sure there's enough room to get near, be heard, and keep the right amount of eye contact (especially if someone uses a wheelchair). They'll also need to check out any routines which might interfere with their talking. They won't want to be interrupted or distracted or overheard by anyone else.

Finding out what kind of assistance may be necessary: Volunteers will need to check out what language or other support people will need: will spoken or sign language be appropriate? Will it be helpful to have someone to interpret or assist with communication?

Establishing an appropriate level of communication: Volunteers will need to do some preliminary talking to find out how best to put the questions so that residents understand what's being asked.

Feeding back: Volunteers will need to be able to check through what residents have said. They will have to choose an appropriate method – reading through, or using diagrams and noting comments.

Finding out: Volunteers will need to be able to identify with the perspective, feelings and understanding of the residents they talk to. This may mean knowing how to find out about the nature of the institution, or the kind of care provision which someone has experienced over the years. If they aren't aware of someone's background then they may misinterpret what they are told.

As you can see, there is a lot more to Lorraine's enquiry than 'just asking a few questions'. It requires a carefully thought-out strategy. That is because of the particular challenges posed by communications in these circumstances. However, it is really just an extension of the discussion about interviewing in Unit 16. In Activity 14 of Unit 16 we drew up a list of guidelines for ethical practice. Look back at this now. What you see listed there is what we described as 'good practice in interpersonal communication ... polite and considerate behaviour'. At one level that is what good communication is always about. But sometimes people need extra help and support, particularly if their level of understanding or ability to speak are restricted in any way.

Because of the sensitivity and sometimes the complexity of communication challenges, care workers need to be aware of their own limitations in such situations. The list above could help you to check on your own preparedness for encounters such as the one in the video. Do you feel more confident about tackling such challenges now?

> **Key points**
>
> - Supporting effective communication means identifying barriers which may be physical, personal, linguistic, cultural, societal, emotional.
>
> - If communication is to be effective there may sometimes be a need for preparation in order to overcome barriers.
>
> - Preparation may involve: checking out and removing physical barriers, finding out how someone prefers to be addressed, finding out what assistance is needed, finding out how best to put questions, finding out about the context in which people live and their experiences there.

The second video sequence looks at another kind of communication challenge. What can happen when someone needs to communicate something private in a public space?

Section 3
Facilitating the communication of sensitive issues

In the next part of the video you'll see Andrew, a care worker, talking to Sean, one of the residents in the home where he works. Andrew has some news for Sean. He's been on a waiting list for a prostate operation for a few months now and suddenly he's been given a date for his operation. Andrew needs to tell him so that he can help him prepare for the operation. Sean spends most of his time sitting in the lounge, so Andrew has to find a way to let him know what's going on without letting everyone else know at the same time. Let's see how he gets on.

Activity 6	**Private talk in a public space**

Allow about 20 minutes

Play Scene 9 through once just so that you have an idea of what happens. Now watch it through again. This time make some notes about Andrew's approach to Sean. You might find it helpful to start with questions like:

(a)   How did Andrew approach Sean?

(b)   How did Sean react?

(c)   Did Sean understand what Andrew was saying to him?

(d)   What were Sean's concerns?

Comment

Andrew thought he had good news for Sean, so he wasn't prepared for his outburst. Why did things go wrong?

(a)   **Approach**: Andrew seems to have forgotten that Sean is hard of hearing – also that not everyone else nearby is as deaf as he is. A lounge is not a place to communicate personal and private information. His first approach to Sean should have been to arrange for them to talk on their own where no one else could overhear them.

Andrew also seems not to realise that he is dealing with a sensitive issue and that he should have thought in advance about how to approach it. There are some differences which he might have thought about: age, background and role for a start. By choosing a public place he's limited himself to a small range of ways of communicating with Sean. (These circumstances restrict the possibilities in terms of tone, facial expression, eye contact and touch.) Though he tries to position himself as close as he can, his clumsy approach means that they are never going to get off to a good start.

(b) **Sean's reactions**: Sean was upset. He expressed his feelings by withdrawing and rejecting Andrew's attempts to talk.

(c) **Did Sean understand?** Effective communication means just that. You'll remember our definition at the start of this unit: 'Communication is *sharing* meaning'. By his insensitive approach Andrew has managed to set up emotional barriers between himself and Sean. Andrew also needs to be aware of how to talk to Sean about his forthcoming operation. He must use a vocabulary that he can understand. He needs to be able to allay Sean's fears about surgery in such a sensitive part of the body.

(d) **Sean's concerns**: We can't know exactly what Sean's concerns are, but we might speculate having observed his reactions. He seems to want to avoid talking about his operation at all, but this may be just his way of expressing his fears about surgery, especially in this area of his body. He may also be concerned that what to him should be a private matter is known to staff, including young women – and now, probably to other residents as well.

Andrew's approach hasn't been helpful. He didn't prepared himself properly and now Sean may refuse to go ahead with an operation which he badly needs. For both their sakes we should give him a second chance to tell Sean the news about his prostate surgery.

Activity 7   Supporting the person in communication

Allow about 15 minutes   Imagine you are a colleague of Andrew's. He has come to you after his difficult encounter with Sean. Somehow he has to make sure Sean knows what the options are for his operation.

How would you advise Andrew to go about approaching Sean a second time?

Andrew might find it helpful to have a list of questions he needs to think about – with action notes against each. There's a table overleaf for you to make notes for Andrew. When you are thinking of questions for the left-hand column the following checklist may be useful:

*   When is the best time to talk to Sean?
*   What exactly does Sean need to be told?
*   Why am I telling him?
*   Where is the best place to talk to Sean?
*   How should I begin to tell him?
*   How can I make sure that he understands what I'm saying?
*   How can I reassure Sean?
*   What do I do if Sean becomes upset?
*   How do I make sure that Sean stays prepared?

(Don't feel you have to cover them all.) To start you off I've filled in the first row.

Questions to think about	What to do
When is the best time to talk to Sean?	Check out his routines and what's going on in the home today.

Questions to think about	What to do

Comment   How much were you able to write in the box? If you found it difficult to think of what to write about, try copying some of the questions from the left-hand column of the table below into your own table. Then have another try at the right-hand column, before reading my version. (As this is a 'skills' unit, it is important do as much as you can with the activities before reading the commentary.)

Here are my notes to compare with what you wrote:

Questions to think about	What to do
When is the best time to talk to Sean?	Check out his routines and what's going on in the home each day.
What exactly does Sean need to be told?	Work out what you need to explain to Sean about what the operation will involve. Will diagrams help? Make sure you know all the relevant details of the arrangements about going into hospital. Since Sean seems not to be at all clear about what the operation involves you'll need to find a way to describe it to him and what happens afterwards in language which he uses and which does not embarrass or confuse him. If you aren't sure yourself then you should find a colleague who knows, or look up the details of the operation and its outcomes in a reference book or nursing magazine. Find out from Sean if he knows the hospital where he'll have his operation; if he doesn't know it then tell him where it is and how he'll be taken there and brought back. Sean has no relatives in England so you might like to reassure him that, if this is what he wants, you'll arrange for someone from the home to visit him while he's there and that the priest will be told that he's going into hospital.
Why am I telling him?	You want to respect his right to knowledge about his needs and the treatments proposed. You want him to be calm, confident and well prepared when he goes to hospital.
Where is the best place to talk to Sean?	Find a spare room where you won't be disturbed or overheard. If Sean's room-mate is in their bedroom, arrange with colleagues to use an office or a treatment room.
How should I begin to tell him?	Don't expect this to be a one-off communication. You may not have much time if the hospital bed comes through suddenly, but you need to start a process of discussing the operation and the arrangements with Sean. Begin by saying that you need to talk to him on his own — maybe reminding him at times before you actually get together.

How can I make sure that he understands what I'm saying?	Sean is hard of hearing and he has some problems with remembering. Telling Sean about the details of the operation means finding a space and somewhere he will feel comfortable asking you questions. It also means listening, actively, to what he says so that you can pick up on what is concerning him. In that way you can be more certain that you are telling him what he wants to know rather than just what you think he needs to know. Active listening also means noticing *how* he talks, so you can get a sense of his feelings about the operation and what it involves.
How can I reassure Sean?	Sean seems to be anxious about the operation. He may also be anxious about having to go into hospital and be among strangers. Reassuring Sean (and making sure that he's understood what you're saying) means making sure that he has eye contact with you. Position yourself reasonably close with enough light for him to be able to see your face. You might touch him to reassure him, squeeze his arm perhaps. Make sure that Sean is aware that if there are things he does not like about his stay in hospital he can complain if he wants to. He has rights as a hospital patient. You might suggest to Sean that you write a note addressed to the staff on his ward with a list of his likes and dislikes. You should write this note together and make sure that he keeps it in a safe place.
What do I do if Sean becomes upset?	Show understanding straightaway by responding in a supportive way. Give him plenty of time to express his feelings. Encourage him to talk about other experiences of hospitals and operations that he may have had. Reassure him that his concerns will be taken seriously and passed on to staff at the hospital – show him that you have noted down anything he feels strongly about. If you feel that you can't deal with his distress on your own ask a colleague to help. (In your record of the meeting include what his reactions were and how you dealt with them.)

How do I make sure that Sean stays prepared?	Make sure he knows he can talk to you about the operation whenever he wants. If you made a note for the hospital staff, go over it with him again.
	Pay special attention to Sean over the next few days before the operation.
	Be prepared to run through the details frequently — remembering to preserve his privacy. He may not remember what you have told him but he still will not want other residents to know his business.

Keep the work from this activity in your K100 portfolio. If you decide to do a VQ in care, this material could provide useful evidence.

Andrew should now be able to prepare Sean well. However his good work may be undone if the hospital staff are not aware of Sean's background and his anxieties. In Unit 14 we noted that medical and other staff may tend to focus more on the patient's physical condition than on the whole person and their identity. Andrew needs to find a way of representing Sean's concerns to the staff on the ward.

Someone in Andrew's situation is not working alone. Anyone working with an older person, either at home or in a care setting, should have access to support of various kinds. Effective communication in such situations includes working with colleagues – communicating your own anxieties and need for support to them, knowing what to ask and who to ask. Andrew could look for:

- colleagues with more experience or specialised training in, for example, medical or nursing care, care of the dying, advocacy and empowerment
- sources of information: reference books, professional magazines and journals in libraries, from organisations specialising in information and support for older people (see Care in the UK).

Andrew and Sean

Before we leave Sean and Andrew, we can draw out some general guidelines for good communications about sensitive issues. We can use the five principles of good practice as our framework.

1 **Enable people to develop their own potential:**
   Providing the time, place and opportunity for someone to raise concerns, ask questions and put over their point of view; ensuring that someone is aware of their rights in different situations.

2 **Enable people to have a voice and be heard:**
   Making sure that anxieties and preferences are represented to those who need to know – both verbally and in written form.

3 **Respect people's beliefs and preferences:**
   Encouraging people to talk about themselves, not making assumptions about preferences, ensuring that preferences once expressed are acted upon (for example Sean may have been brought up an Irish Catholic but he may not wish to see a priest).

4 **Promote and support people's rights to appropriate services:**
   Finding the right language and providing opportunities to discuss conditions and treatments. Older people's medical needs may be overlooked, particularly if they find it difficult to communicate their own feelings or describe symptoms. They may also need to be supported in their right to treatment.

5 **Respect people's privacy and rights to confidentiality:**
   Ensuring that when necessary there is time and a place which is acceptable to a service user where it is possible to talk in privacy; making sure that it is clear what information is to be treated as confidential and what is to be passed on for others to read or hear.

Key points

- Effective communication means paying close attention to *how* the communication will take place.

- *Where* the communication takes place may be an important consideration.

- Sometimes people's emotions or reactions may prevent effective communication.

- Effective communication means *listening* to what people say as well as observing their behaviour.

- Sometimes people need time to absorb the information which is being communicated.

- Effective communication means working with colleagues and other team members with different areas of expertise if particular concerns are to be understood.

Section 4
Managing communication within a group

In this section we change our focus and look at communication with a group of under-fives. They are preparing for the transition from family centre to primary school. This is a situation in which the needs of individuals have to be supported within a group setting. In fact the group setting is in itself a learning experience for the children.

Our case involves a multicultural family centre in an inner city area, run by Barnardos for the local authority. The children at this centre have been referred because they or their families have special needs – usually identified through a multidisciplinary referral process and with social services carried out at a specialist unit in a nearby hospital.

We're going to look at a short episode taken from a session with a group of children in a pre-school group. It is lunch-time and Sandra, the day care worker, is getting the children ready to eat together. The six children are all rising five. It's June and the intention is that they will be entering mainstream schools in September. This is the day they are in 'pre-school', which means setting up tasks and activities that link directly to the school curriculum and the sorts of skills they'll need if they are to manage independently in a school setting. They've been chosen to work together. Other children of the same age and younger are in another room in a larger group while another group of two children who are not suited to group care are with two day care workers on their own in another room. The place, the worker and the children have all been anonymised, though the events described in the case study are all real.

Sandra is a qualified nursery nurse and experienced children's worker who has been at the centre for three years. There are six children: two boys and four girls, Desmond, Kofi, Keisha, Sharon, Toksi and Sophie.

This takes us back to our discussions of group work in Unit 15. Sandra has a complex set of tasks. She needs to be able to:

*   identify and keep in mind the individual communication skills of each child
*   observe and interpret what is going on amongst members of the group
*   find ways to support and develop communication skills between group members
*   shape the way the group works so that it is facilitative to communication.

Activity 8   **Lunch-time at East View**

Allow about 20 minutes   Read through the case study below. As you do, underline all the verbs to do with communication (asks, tells, sings etc.).

Case study

It's getting towards the end of the morning with the pre-school group. The group uses a space in the middle of the family centre building. Doors lead off to meeting rooms, play areas, treatment rooms, offices and the kitchen area. The space is set out like a school classroom for reception-age children, with low tables and chairs, a book area with a rug, a play house and storage shelves at child height. The children have been doing jigsaw puzzles, worksheets, drawing and activities with numbers and colour recognition. Now Sandra is getting them to put things away while she helps Toksi with her jigsaw and talks to her about the picture she's been making with the pieces. She asks Desmond to put away the crayons while some of the others, Sophie, Kofi and Keisha, carry on doing some letter recognition on the worksheets with another day care worker who has joined in for a short while. Sharon is sitting on the rug looking at a book.

Sandra is organising the putting away so that all the children are involved in the process, either packing away the equipment they've been using or getting themselves ready for lunch. She manages the process through setting distinct tasks and using the space in the room.

She works with the children by asking them to do various tasks. She praises them regularly and individually when they complete a task. When Desmond has put away a set of numbers he and the others have been looking at, she tells him he can choose a book and join the others on the rug in front of the book case. Toksi follows him once she's finished doing a puzzle and put it back in its box.

Sophie and Sharon are on the rug as well with Keisha. They're supposed to be looking at books but seem to be more concerned with keeping Keisha out of what they are doing. Things could get difficult as verbal seems to be spilling over into physical, with some pushing going on. Sandra is busy putting everything away now, tidying up and getting a table ready for them to sit at by putting a cloth over it and arranging six chairs round it.

She tells Kofi to put his book away and to go for a 'wee wee'. She helps him to undo the bib on his trousers and tells him to wash his hands before he comes back. Everybody else is told to sit down on the rug. Sophie and Sharon are teasing Toksi about a book. Sandra tells Sharon and Sophie to get their own books and tells Desmond to go to the bathroom, 'do a wee wee' and wash his hands. She tells Sophie to get a tissue and blow her nose, which she does. Sharon and Keisha are 'reading' aloud from their books. Desmond and Kofi have come back and are sitting at the lunch table talking to each other. Sandra tells Keisha and Sharon to go and 'do a wee wee and wash hands'. She gives Desmond and Kofi a drink of water.

Toksi asks Sandra about a book and Sandra reads out the names of the children whose pictures are in the book. Keisha and Sharon are still in the toilet area but haven't been yet. Sandra tells them to hurry up because Sophie and Toksi are waiting. Kofi and Desmond are at the table playing with their glasses of water, Desmond with some encouragement from Kofi. Sandra notices and calls out to Desmond. Sandra looks at the books and talks to the children about what to read after lunch. Tells Sophie and Toksi to 'walk' to the toilet, gets Keisha and Sharon back and tells them to walk to sit at the table. She gives Sophie and Sharon drinks and asks Desmond if he has drunk his water. Tells Toksi and Sophie to sit down and have a drink.

They are sitting like this:

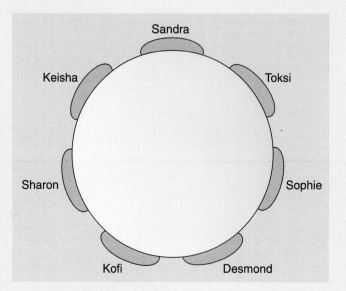

Now that they are sitting down together and Desmond has finished having a drink she tells him to give everyone a fork: 'one like that and you give one to everyone'. He picks up enough forks and goes round the table putting a fork in front of each person. Toksi wants to do the knives. Sandra tells her to sit with her feet under the table. Kofi gives out the knives, starting with Toksi. Sandra tells everyone to sit with 'hands on your lap'. They do this. She goes round and straightens everyone's cutlery.

There's some time before dinner is actually served so she asks everyone what they did today. She asks Toksi what she did. She says she played with puzzles and did the worksheets. The children are all very quiet as she asks each in turn. She asks Sophie what she did, looking at her directly. She's quiet, so Sandra says that she did some puzzles and some counting. She asks Desmond, looks at him and prompts him: 'You did something with colours'. Asks Kofi to tell her quickly what he did and tells Toksi to listen, 'Tell me about the book we read this morning, what was it about?' Kofi says 'school'. She praises him, 'Well done'. Asks Sharon what she did, 'Did you do a puzzle and drawing?' Asks Keisha what she did at pre-school'. Keisha says 'shopping'. Sandra says no, at pre-school. She answers and Sandra says 'Good girl'.

Desmond drops his fork. Sandra says it's dirty now and tells him to get another one.

Dinner comes in on a trolley and is served onto the table. Sandra serves everyone with a slice of flan and calls Keisha to get a plate to give to Sophie. She gives Toksi her plate. Keisha gives a plate to Desmond, to Kofi and then to Sharon. She tells the children they can start. Sandra serves a plate of food then leaves the children and another day care worker, Jane, her line manager, takes her place. Jane explains that Sandra is going on a break. The children know Jane and greet her. Jane asks them if they had a nice morning. The children ask what the food is and she tells them. The children talk among themselves about mummies and daddies. Sharon says her mum has bought her some socks. Jane tells Sophie not to interrupt Sharon, encourages Toksi to eat and asks Keisha if she would like some more.

Jane talks about Keisha's birthday last week and Desmond joins in. Sophie and Toksi are doing less talking and more eating. At times the children are quiet and eating.

Jane asks if anyone wants more and serves those who do.

Jane goes out of the room for a few moments and the children talk to each other. Kofi tells Desmond he's got a dirty mouth (food). Jane comes back, sits down and asks the children if they've been to the school they're going to in September. The children all try to tell her things. Toksi tells a story, Jane says she didn't understand and asks her to tell it again. Sophie says she's had to have her blood looked at. Jane says that's something that she has to do a lot. Sharon says she has to go to hospital. They all talk about going to the doctor. Kofi says he fell down and he had to go.

Jane helps Desmond to cut up his food and asks Sophie to eat more. Kofi says Sharon and Desmond have dirty mouths. Jane says, 'we can all clean ourselves when we've finished'. The children start making noises and laughing across the table. Jane asks Toksi about her school and going to church. Toksi talks about church. Sharon says she goes to church. Jane tells Toksi to put her hand down while Sharon is speaking. Toksi says 'Let's go out after dinner'. Jane says it's up to Sandra.

Desmond says ' Me go to Dad's'. Jane agrees and says he sometimes goes to Stuart's house, doesn't he? Desmond says he went to the seaside. General talking and Jane asks Toksi to wait while other people are talking.

Kofi says he wrote on the wall and keeps saying this. Jane asks him to say it again and asks him if his mother was cross. She asks each child if they want more pie and if they have finished. She clears away the plates.

Pudding is trifle. She tells them what it's called and how it's made. She asks them who wants some. Nobody seems very keen. Desmond puts his hand up and says, 'Me'. Sophie passes a plate to Desmond. Kofi says he would like some. Toksi and Sophie each say, 'OK I'll have a little'. Asks Sharon, she passes a plate across. Keisha says she'll have some, but 'No jelly, just the top'. Kofi says it's nice.

Jane says 'Shall we save some for Sandra?' Children all say no, then Toksi says that wouldn't be very nice. The children say what they don't like about the pudding.

Sandra comes by and says, 'Nice dinner?' The children ask her if she wants any pudding. She says no and they can eat it all. Toksi tells them about how she was sick after eating too much pizza.

Jane tells Desmond to wash his face now that he's finished. Sharon is spreading food on her face with her spoon. Toksi goes to wash herself and falls over; Jane looks to see. Sophie says 'Sorry' though she was nowhere near.

Jane tells Desmond to sit down on the rug with a book and sends Sophie to get washed. Jane smiles at Kofi who is finishing his lunch. Toksi sings 'One, two, three four five'. Sophie and Sharon run back in and get books. Jane sends Keisha to the toilets. Sophie says she'll read to the others but Sharon says 'Not to Desmond'. Desmond gets his own book; he says he'll read to them. The children are saying words to each other. Keisha joins with a book. Kofi says he's finished now and Jane tells him to get washed. She clears up the table.

Sharon and Sophie are arguing about a book. Jane asks who had it first. She tells everyone to sit on the carpet with a book. The four girls all lie down in a row with their books. Toksi is 'reading' to them. Kofi and Dennis try to join in beside them. The girls start chanting. Toksi organises everyone so that they're all on the rug.

Sandra is back now and finishes off clearing up the dinner table, folding up the table cloth. Kofi points out a bike to Desmond in his book. Sandra comes and sits in a chair next to the rug and says 'Books away'. She gets ready to read the children a story.

Comment   If you did as I suggested, you should have underlined a lot of words. Look back quickly over your underlining. What strikes you?

I was struck by just how much communicating there was – between Sandra and the children (as individuals and as a group), between individual children, between groups of children and between the day care workers. The children in this group have different language levels, some have language delay.

I also noticed different forms of communication – verbal and non verbal, pushing, raising hands, listening quietly. There were also different styles: quiet voices, raised voices, laughing, arguing, singing and calling out. Often there were many different forms and styles going on at the same time. But sometimes one person held the attention of the whole group.

But most of all I was impressed by how systematic and regularised a lot of Sandra's communications were. They had a distinct rhythm and pattern and were clearly tuned to an overall purpose.

If communication is about sharing meaning then someone in Sandra's situation is probably using lunch-time as an opportunity to convey more than one message to the children.

Activity 9   ## Communication with a purpose

Allow about 5 minutes   What do you think Sandra was trying to achieve through her use of communications? And what do you think the children were actually learning in this session?

Comment   It might seem that these children were being told what to do most of the time and offered activity within a fairly limited set of routines. However, these are four-year-olds whose backgrounds and reasons for referral might have led to them being excluded from mainstream schools. They are being prepared for what will be a big change for them in terms of the size of the groups they will be mixing in with, the other children they will meet and the type of environment that school offers in terms of care and support. They will be encountering a whole new culture. If they are going to cope in mainstream school they will need to be able to act independently and to be responsible for themselves – for example, going to the toilet on their own, cutting up and handling food, managing drinks, being clean and finding appropriate activities. They will also need to be capable of taking part in group activities, to develop a sense of co-operation, like managing themselves at meal times without disrupting the other children, being helpful, being aware of what's going on and aware of other people, being able to do things unsupervised and not fight among themselves. Sandra is also aiming to help them to develop their concentration and understanding.

Looking back to the five principles of good practice yet again, you could say that all five are relevant but that in particular, Sandra and Jane, through the communication strategies which they have adopted, are enabling this particular group of young children to develop their own potential.

There is another level of communication which is of course involved in what we've seen described. As a care worker Sandra needs to be able to account for what she does. She needs to be able to describe what feel like tightly planned packages of work and ensure that she notes down anything unusual or important in developmental terms relating to each child. This information will be needed to refine each child's care plan in preparation for the transition to school. The children take a pre-school folder with them when they transfer into mainstream or other settings. Sandra will need to have kept a record for other workers with whom the children and their parents may come into contact.

Activity 10   ## Identifying skills

Allow about 15 minutes   In the table overleaf I have listed six examples of communications taken from the case study. Read through the case study again and when you come to the examples, make a note of what you think is being communicated to the individual and to the group.

I have left space for a couple of examples of your own. (You could include non-verbal communications.)

Example	What is being communicated?
1 Sandra tells Desmond to put away the crayons and numbers	
2 Sandra tells Kofi to put his book away and go to the toilet	
3 Sandra asks the children what they did today as they wait for food	
4 Sandra calls Keisha to take plates of food to the other children	
5 Jane says 'we can all clean ourselves when we've finished'	
6 Sandra is clearing up while the children are reading on the rug	

Comment   Here is what I noticed:

Examples	What is being communicated?
1 Sandra tells Desmond to put away the crayons and numbers	1 She's letting Desmond know that she trusts him to put things away in the right place; she's letting the others know that she trusts Desmond to do this; the others hear that this is an appropriate task for someone to be doing at this stage in the morning.
2 Sandra tells Kofi to put his book away and go to the toilet	2 She's letting Kofi know that he can do this on his own (apart from his trouser buttons); she's signalling that getting ready for lunch is beginning; she implies that they already know what to do.
3 Sandra asks the children what they did today as they wait for food	3 She's giving them individual attention within the group; she's encouraging them to listen to each other; she's encouraging awareness of each other and of the group as a whole; she's making sure that everyone has practice at saying something within the group setting; she's reminding them what they did this morning that is relevant to pre-school activities, to reinforce learning about school routines.
4 Sandra calls Keisha to take plates of food to the other children	4 She's letting Keisha know that she's competent to do this job; she's letting the others know that this is how you help people and that Keisha is competent to do this; by giving plates to the others Keisha is seen as a helpful person by them and part of a co-operative group.
5 Jane says 'we can all clean ourselves when we've finished'	5 She's gently letting Kofi know that being 'dirty' is something that can happen to anyone when they're eating, that it can easily be sorted out, and there is a time for that in the routine.
6 Sandra is clearing up while the children are reading on the rug	6 They can see what she is doing and they know what they should be doing even when they aren't being told what to do.

In this part of the block you've looked at different care situations in which skills in communication play an important part. We have focused on three areas in particular:

- *Supporting effective communication:* here we watched a small group of residents and staff in a hospital and saw how, in spite of communication difficulties, the members of the group worked together to support effective communication.

- *Facilitating communication of sensitive issues:* we looked at the difficulties which Andrew faced as he tried to talk to Sean about his prostate operation.

- *Managing communications within a group:* we looked at day care workers, Sandra and Jane, working with a group of under-fives and saw their purposeful approach to communication.

At the start we also mentioned a fourth area:

- Developing an awareness of how your own behaviour may empower or disempower the people you are seeking to help and support.

This fourth area has been implicit in much of what we have discussed. It leads us to Activity 11.

Activity 11   **Empowering and disempowering communication**

Allow about 15 minutes   Pick out a situation in which you have been involved in helping another person or a group of people. Was your behaviour empowering or disempowering? What could you have done to be more empowering?

(a) Write a short description of the situation you are thinking of.

(b) Get a sheet of paper and write 'Communication' at the top. Then draw a line down the middle. Write as headings for the two columns 'Being disempowering' and 'Being empowering'.

(c) Just to remind yourself of some points about communication, skim back through Sections 1 to 4 and, bearing in mind the situation you have chosen, make notes under the two headings.

Include this sheet in your personal file.

Comment   I hope that working through these exercises has helped to raise your awareness of the importance of communication skills for care workers, and has given you some ideas for developing your own skills.

> **Key points**
>
> - In a group setting it may be important to support the communication needs of particular individuals.
>
> - Sometimes communication may be a means of conveying a number of different messages.
>
> - Managing communication in a group may be a way to develop an awareness of others, skills in co-operative behaviour, independence and the development of individual potential.

Section 5
Number work skills

In Unit 14 you heard Paul Theobald's account of the impact of the AIDS epidemic on himself and his friends, and of his current work with London Lighthouse. You can now get a fuller picture of the scale of the epidemic and whom it has affected. We are going to look at statistics published by the Department of Health, showing the number of cases recorded in England between 1982 and 1994 and the likely sources of infection.

The table looks rather complicated and it takes time to work out what all the categories mean but, as before, if you take it a little at a time you will find it becomes quite clear.

Activity 12

Allow about 5 minutes

Taking in the big picture

(a)   How many male AIDS cases were reported in 1993?

(b)   How many women were reported as AIDS cases in 1994?

(c)   How many men died of AIDS between 1982 and 1994?

Comment

(a)   The answer is 1,281. You will see at the top of the first column of figures that it covers the 12 months of 1993 – and that it deals with male cases. The total number of male cases is given at the bottom of the column.

(b)   The answer is 181. Columns 3 and 4 show the cases for January to December 1994. Column 4 shows the female cases. Again the total is at the bottom.

(c)   The answer is 6,033. For the 12 year period from 1982 to 1994 you need to look at the four columns over to the right. In these columns both cases and deaths are shown. You need to find the column for male deaths and look for the total at the bottom.

You have found your way into the table now, so we can start to explore some of the detail.

Activity 13

Allow about 10 minutes

Getting into the detail

(a)   Over the 12 year period covered by this table, how have women most commonly acquired the AIDS virus?

(b)   Did this change at all in the most recent two years?

(c)   Did similar numbers of men become infected this way?

(d)   Has this been the most common source of AIDS in men?

(e)   Look at the row headings over at the left of the table. Why do you think some of the headings are indented to the right?

(f)   Are 'high risk' partners the main source of AIDS contracted through heterosexual intercourse? What does high risk mean?

(g)   Does the number of AIDS cases show any signs of decline?

(h)   Roughly what proportion of AIDS cases had ended in death by the end of 1994?

Table 1   AIDS cases and known deaths by exposure and date of report, England, 1982–31 December 1994

How persons probably acquired the virus	Jan 1993-Dec 1993		Jan 1994-Dec 1994		Jan 1982-Dec 1994			
	Cases		Cases		Male		Female	
	Male	Female	Male	Female	Cases	Deaths	Cases	Deaths
Sexual intercourse:								
Between men	1007	-	1092	-	7095	4970	-	-
Between men and women								
'High risk' partner*	4	21	6	16	31	16	82	48
Other partner abroad**	108	94	137	97	553	301	378	180
Other partner UK	17	10	12	9	54	32	41	28
Partner risk not known	2	-	11	3	15	4	3	-
Injecting drug use (IDU)	44	29	68	24	255	154	111	59
IDU and sexual intercourse								
Between men	22	-	26	-	154	97	-	-
Blood								
Blood factor (eg haemophiliacs)	49	-	65	-	407	341	5	3
Blood or tissue transfer (eg transfusion)								
Abroad	3	12	2	2	12	5	40	23
UK	3	2	2	3	19	14	21	18
Mother to child	11	12	22	22	67	35	68	32
Other/undetermined	11	2	10	5	83	64	16	10
Total	1281	182	1453	181	8745	6033	765	401

* Men and women who had sex with injecting drug users, or with those infected through blood factor treatment or blood transfusion, and women who had sex with bisexual men.

** Includes persons without other identified risks who are from, or who have lived in, countries where the major route of HIV-1 transmission is through sexual intercourse between men and women.

(Department of Health, 1995, Table 6.1, p. 160)

Comment   (a)   In each of the three columns for female cases the largest category by a long way is sexual intercourse with a man from abroad. (The note at the foot of the table refers to partners 'who are from, or who have lived in,' countries where HIV-1 is mainly transmitted through heterosexual sex.)

          (b)   No – the figures in this category have remained high.

          (c)   Somewhat larger numbers of men are reported as having been infected this way.

          (d)   No, these figures are small compared to the numbers of men infected through homosexual intercourse, where the figures are at least ten times as high.

          (e)   The main headings start over to the left. Those shifted to the right are sub-headings – and those shifted further to the right are sub-sub-headings. So the first five rows of figures are all to do with sexual intercourse. But sexual intercourse is divided into two categories – between men, and between men and women. Then between men and women is itself divided into four categories.

          (f)   Relatively few AIDS cases are the result of heterosexual intercourse with partners classified as 'high risk'. You need to look at the footnote to see what 'high risk partner' means. It means people who inject drugs, or have been infected through blood treatments, or are bisexual men. The fact that fewer people are infected by 'high risk' partners does not mean that these partners are not 'risky'. It means that there are a lot more sexual relationships with partners who are not drug users, bisexual or have had blood treatments – so they are not 'obviously' high risk. In other words, a lot of carriers are not in the obvious risk categories.

          (g)   No – the number of cases is higher for 1994 than for 1993 (though the number of female cases dropped by one). If you add the men and the women together for 1993 and 1994 it comes to about 3,000 cases. Adding the men to the women for 1982 to 1994 gives a total of about 9,500. So nearly one-third of the cases over a 12-year period have been reported in the last two of those years. This suggests that the numbers were rising pretty rapidly.

          (h)   The total number of cases reported is, as we have just seen, about 9,500. If we add the male and female deaths together the total is just over 6,400. Six is two-thirds of nine. So roughly two-thirds of AIDS cases had ended in death by the end of 1994.

We have looked at the sexual intercourse related infections, but what about the other categories?

Activity 14   **More detail**

Allow about 5 minutes   (a)   Is injecting with drugs a significant source of AIDS?

          (b)   Is it a more significant source for men than for women?

          (c)   Is it more significant than blood treatments?

          (d)   In most categories there are more male cases than female, but not in the mother to child category. Why is this?

          (e)   About one-third of mother to child infections for the whole 12 years were reported in 1994. Why this dramatic increase?

Comment   (a)   255 men and 111 women have been infected through injecting drugs over the 12 years. 366 people is a lot – but not compared with the 9,500 infected altogether. (If we round up 366 to 400 and 9,500 to 10,000, we get 400 out of 10,000 – knocking two zeros off each figure gives 4 out of 100, which is 4 per cent.) So injecting drugs *is* a significant source, but not nearly as significant as infection through intercourse.

   (b)   Well over twice as many men have been infected through injecting drugs. But well over ten times more men than have been infected altogether. (8,745 as compared with 765.) So the proportion of men infected by injecting drugs (about 3 per cent) is much lower than the proportion of women infected this way (about 15 per cent). So it is a *less* significant source for men.

   (c)   Blood factor treatment alone has caused considerably more cases than drug injection.

   (d)   Most of the categories are related in some way to lifestyle and habits and it seems that men run more risks of infection than women do. However transmission from mother to child is unrelated to any behaviour by the child or to its sex. So in each year the figure for male and female infections through the mother is roughly the same.

   (e)   By the end of 1994, of the 765 female AIDS cases 401 had died. So there were 364 women with AIDS. As the number of women with AIDS increases (two-thirds contracted through heterosexual sex) more children are likely to be born with AIDS. (Twice as many in 1994 as in 1993.)

Study skills: Using a spreadsheet

Incidentally, if you have access to a computer and a 'spreadsheet' program, playing around with tables is wonderfully easy. You can get it to work out all kinds of percentages and different ways of adding up totals. If you do have a spreadsheet program but haven't got round to using it, do get someone to show you how – or buy a book. It will transform your work with tables and also produce beautiful charts and graphs in minutes.

We have given this table a pretty good working over now. But it is not actually presented in the best way for helping us to see the overall picture and spot trends. For that we need to turn the figures into percentages.

I also subtracted the 1993 and 1994 figures from the 1982–94 totals, so that I had the 1982–92 totals. That gave me the table opposite.

Table 2   AIDS cases by exposure category, shown as percentages

	Male			Female		
	1982-92	*1993*	*1994*	*1982-92*	*1993*	*1994*
Sex between men	83	79	75			
Sex between men and women: high risk partner				11	12	9
Sex between men and women: partner abroad	5	8	9	47	52	54
Sex between men and women: partner UK		1	1	5	5	5
Sex between men and women: risk not known			1			2
Injecting drug use	2	3	5	14	16	13
Injecting drugs and sex between men	2	2	2			
Blood factor	5	4	4	1		
Blood tissue transfer abroad				6	7	1
Blood tissue transfer UK				4	1	2
Mother to child	1	1	2	8	7	12
Other	1	1	1	2	1	3
Total cases (=100%)	6,011	1,281	1,453	402	182	181

Activity 15   Looking for trends

Allow about 5 minutes

(a)   Can you see any trends in the figures – any changes to the pattern of the ways people become infected?

(b)   How do men and women differ in terms of the ways they catch AIDS?

Comment   (a)   The proportion of infections through heterosexual intercourse with a partner from abroad is increasing for both men and women. For men the proportion infected through drug injections also seems to be increasing. Correspondingly, the proportion of men infected through intercourse with other men seems to be decreasing (although numbers are actually increasing, as the first table shows). Other changes seem to be more fluctuating.

(b)   More than three-quarters of men catch AIDS through intercourse with other men. However increasing numbers are infected through intercourse with women from abroad (nearly 10 per cent now). The other two significant sources are drug injecting and blood factor treatment, together accounting for nearly 10 per cent. With women more than half now catch AIDS through intercourse with men from abroad. Injecting with drugs is the next most common source at around 15 per cent. Sex with high risk men accounts for about 10 per cent. And infection by mother is the next highest category.

Study skills: Digging about in the data

You have spent a lot of time now with this one set of data. What skills have you developed? This table may look rather different from others you have seen before; the numbers are unevenly spaced; there are blanks; there are some very small numbers and some very large. Altogether it is quite a challenge to find your way in. So, one skill is working in gradually by asking questions and looking for answers.

Also these figures are quite difficult to 'react' to. They look almost random at first sight. It's hard to get a picture in your head of what they are telling you. But now you have seen that there is actually a great deal you can dig out of this one table. You just keep on asking questions and looking. That is another important skill – nosing your way around a set of figures, checking one against another; deciding whether they make sense, whether they are surprising, and what you could write down as a worthwhile 'finding'. It's not something you'd do as a daily pastime (unless you're a real enthusiast), but now and again it can be very informative. You just need the confidence.

Section 6
Back to the K100 examination

We began to talk about the K100 exam at the end of Block 3. Now we continue the process of helping you get into the right frame of mind. You can be pretty confident of doing yourself justice, provided you think calmly and strategically ahead of the event. To help you keep things in proportion read Sections 1 and 2 of Chapter 7 of *The Good Study Guide* now.

Study skills: Cutting exams down to size

As you can see from the passage you have just read in *The Good Study Guide*, it is easy to get over anxious about an exam. This can lead you to avoid thinking about it, so that you fail to prepare yourself properly. It can also lead you to panic, so that you stop approaching things sensibly. That is why it is very important to recognise that a lot of the common fears we have about exams are irrational – although they may gain wide circulation as myths, passed on from one generation of anxious students to the next. It is far more helpful to turn the whole thing round and think of the exam as something you can get a lot of value from. Remind yourself that you have paid for it. It's yours. Make it work for you. You have already invested a great deal of time and energy into studying K100. If you approach the exam in the right way it will help you build on that investment, so that you come to know and understand the course a great deal better.

Section 7
Developing writing skills

I hope you feel that you are making progress with your writing skills as you work your way through K100. For a student it is possibly the most important set of skills of all, since you are assessed by what you write. And it may also be the most transferable set of skills, since being able to write in a clear, logical and well informed way is useful in lots of situations. You have completed Chapter 5 of *The Good Study Guide*, where you looked in detail at what good writing is (i.e. what you are aiming to produce in your own essays). You have also read the first three sections of Chapter 6 about treating essay writing as a craft which consists of a series of stages, each with its own skills and strategies. Now we turn to a specific area of skill, to do with making your essay easy to read and compelling in its thrust.

> **Study skills: Making your essay flow**
>
> The theme of Unit 17 is communication – 'sharing meaning'. But if you are communicating in writing, how do you get your readers to share the meaning that is in your head? How do you make them see the logic that connects your ideas? How do you keep them in touch with your overall purpose as you move forward through the essay? That is the topic of Section 4 in Chapter 6 of *The Good Study Guide*. Read it now, and do take the time to do the activities, since that is how you will develop your skills.

I hope you feel you have a heightened awareness now of the craft that goes into making writing flow easily for readers. In fact this is a good moment to consolidate that insight by following up the suggestion just before the box at the bottom of p. 186.

Activity 16 | **Communicating ideas in writing**

Allow about 20 minutes

Select an article you enjoyed from the Course Reader or the Offprints Book and repeat the activities on pp. 177–8 and p. 183 of *The Good Study Guide*.

See whether the same conclusions can be drawn as from the Gardner article.

Comment | Did you pick up any new ideas by looking at a different article? Do you feel you now have a few new tricks to try out in TMA 04? There are no absolute answers regarding making your writing flow. A lot of the available linking and signposting devices are pretty basic and widely used. But the particular ways you combine them give your writing its distinctive character.

End of block assignment

Now to your own effort at 'communicating' to your tutor what you have learnt from Block 4 – TMA 04. I hope thinking about 'flow' helps.

Study skills: Study diary

Block 4 has made a lot of use of video and audio cassettes. It has also discussed the benefits of group processes. Perhaps these would be interesting themes for your study diary notes. How well do you learn from each? Do you need to try out any new ideas? You might also want to make a note of your feelings right now about the exam. Otherwise just keep recording and reflecting on what has not gone as planned and what has gone well, and any ideas to try out as you tackle Block 5.

References

Department of Health (1995) *On the State of The Public Health: The Annual Report of the Chief Medical Officer of the Department of Health for the Year 1994*, HMSO.

Kelly, J.C. (1981) *A Philosophy of Communication*, The Centre for the Study of Communication and Culture, London.

Ryan, T. and Walker, R. (1993) *Life Story Work*, British Agencies for Fostering and Adoption, London.

Acknowledgements

Grateful acknowledgement is made to the following source for permission to reproduce material in this unit:

Table 1: Department of Health 1994, *On the State of the Public Health: The Annual Report of the Chief Medical Officer of Health for the Year 1994,* © Crown Copyright. Reproduced with the permission of the Controller of Her Majesty's Stationery Office.

Grateful acknowledgement is also made to the following sources for permission to reproduce the illustrations on the front cover of this block: *all* Sally and Richard Greenhill except *top right* Brenda Prince/Format and *bottom right* John Birdsall Photography.